THE BRIDGES OF WALES

The Bridges of Wales

Gwyndaf Breese

ISBN: 0-86381-667-3

Cover design: Sian Parri

First published in 2001 by
Gwasg Carreg Gwalch, 12 Iard yr Orsaf, Llanrwst, Wales LL26 0EH
℡ 01492 642031 🖷 01492 641502
✆ books@carreg-gwalch.co.uk   Internet: www.carreg-gwalch.co.uk

This book is dedicated to my sister
Brythonwen,
who somehow managed to convince me
that the end result justified the
painstaking research and seemingly endless travel.

Acknowledgements

I am indebted to many friends and relatives who assisted me during the preparation of this book, in particular William Traherne who joined in the research work with enthusiasm. A much travelled person, he frequently swamped me with information on scraps of paper relating to inscriptions and other titbits about bridges picked up on his journeys around Wales.

Many thanks to others too numerous to mention by name, who supplied photographs and information about bridges in their locality, long before I was able to visit them myself, all of which made the research so much easier.

The archivists of the various establishments consulted were, as usual, both helpful and efficient, guiding me through numerous files on the subject in their possession. To them also, my grateful thanks.

A fo ben, bid bont.
(Ail Gainc Y Mabinogi)

He who would be leader, be a bridge.
(Second Branch of Y Mabinogi)

Pont Menai

Uchelgaer uwch y weilgi, – gyr y byd
Ei gerbydau drosti,
Chwithau holl longau'r lli
Ewch o dan ei chadwyni.

(Dewi Wyn o Eifion)

Menai Bridge

Lofty fort that spans the sea, – and the world's
Wheels speed across thee,
You the ships that sail the sea
Go under links so gracefully.

Contents

Introduction

Wales is a small country that possesses a wealth of natural beauty, and places of historical interest. Together, these have attracted tourists from all over Britain and abroad for over two hundred years. Its mountains and rugged terrain were explored by countless numbers of Victorian travel writers, many of whom published vivid accounts of their journeys. Some, like George Borrow's notable *Wild Wales*, are still in print one hundred and fifty years later. In the early years of the 19th century J.G. Wood wrote *The Principal Rivers of Wales*, which was followed some years later by the less well received *Cambria Depicta* from the pen of Edward Pugh.

Records of journeys into Wales began as far back as the 12th century, when Giraldus Cambrensis accompanied Archbishop Baldwin into the 'wilderness' beyond Offa's Dyke. Their mission was to canvas support for the Crusades. John Leyland made a similar journey in the 16th century, acting as the King's emissary. His brief was to seek out any treasures hidden away after the dissolution of the monasteries. Daniel Defoe was among the first to arrive as a 'proper' tourist, but he found the mountains overpowering and the climate not to his liking. It was left to Thomas Pennant, who travelled extensively through North Wales in the latter part of the 18th century, to put the country on the tourist maps.

Artists also flocked into Wales during the first half of the 19th century. Few were as prolific as Henry Gastineau, who arrived in the 1820s, and his *Wales Illustrated* includes over one hundred and fifty prints of well established 'beauty spots'.

As Wales grew in popularity with tourists, all its main attractions became well documented. In recent years books have appeared describing its mountains, castles, waterfalls, legends, ghosts, shipwrecks, aircrashes and battles, to name but a few. With such a wide coverage, it seemed unlikely that anything had been overlooked, until quite by chance I discovered that there was not a comprehensive guide in print relating to the large number of ancient bridges to be found within Wales.

Further research, however, uncovered a little known publication by Edward Jervoise who, in 1926, commenced on the monumental task of recording all the bridges in England and Wales considered to be 'ancient'. The work, carried out on behalf of the 'Society For the Protection of Ancient Buildings', was spread over a six year period and published in four volumes. During 1931 and 1932, he visited all the bridges considered to be ancient in Wales and the west of England, and in 1936, *Ancient*

9

Bridges of Wales and the West of England was published, the last book in the series.

Jervoise inspected over five thousand bridges in all, which resulted in almost three hundred in Wales and England being scheduled as Ancient Monuments. His book has remained the classic work on Welsh bridges, and a facsimile edition was published by E.P. Publishing in 1976. Of the ninety illustrations in the book, almost sixty were within Wales, confirming that a wealth of fascinating bridges are waiting to be rediscovered.

Since Jervoise carried out his survey, Wales has seen considerable changes in its road and rail network, which has resulted in the destruction of many interesting bridges.

It is not my intention to record all the bridges in Wales; that would be well beyond the scope of this book. Neither is it my aim to confine my attention to those bridges termed 'ancient', which presumably would include only 'listed' structures. Many bridges considered by Jervoise to be 'modern' are now, over sixty years later, worthy of re-examination, and it is my intention to record all those that might prove to be of interest. For that reason I have looked at railway bridges and viaducts, aqueducts and, to a lesser degree, canal bridges as well. Also included are some of the 'twenties type' ferroconcrete bridges, of which there are a few such masterpieces.

The drought that lasted during the period of my fieldwork allowed me to examine underneath many bridges, which would otherwise have been difficult or, in some cases, impossible. I have relied heavily on the work of others as far as statistics and historical facts are concerned.

In all, some two hundred bridges, viaducts, and aqueducts were checked, and there are of course many more that could, and perhaps should, have been included. Time and sanity decided that a halt had to be called somewhere. There is as large a selection of illustrations as possible, which covers a cross section of antique prints, postcards, old photographs, and paintings. In cases where the bridge still retains much of its original form, a recent photograph is probably the best record. There are probably some interesting bridges in remote corners of Wales of which I am unaware, or may have been unable to visit so as to record their existence in enough detail to include them here. The bridges that are now under preservation orders are, hopefully, safe from destruction, but there are more waiting to be discovered and recorded.

Some of the bridges described are difficult to locate, and six figure map references are given rather than the 'turn right at the phone box and straight past the pub' type of direction. Assuming that some are a digit out, they will still guide the searcher to within a hundred yards (100 metres) or so of the bridge in question.

The 1:25,000 Pathfinder maps, being on a large scale, tend to be expensive since they cover a relatively small area. But they are easy to read, and record some of the named bridges. The locations are recorded is six figures, e.g. 538052. The first three digits give the 'across' point; the last three digits give the vertical point. The figures in brackets, e.g. (162) give the relevant O.S. Landranger series map number.

It should be pointed out that a number of the bridges are on private land, and permission MUST be obtained before visiting them. There were a number of instances when I was refused permission to view a bridge, particularly if it was sited on a large estate. Perhaps if I had arrived driving a Range Rover and dressed in tweeds, the response might have been more favourable.

Many of the bridges described by Jervoise are, thankfully, still in existence. My first task was to discover how many had survived, and their present condition. Jervoise had been guided by a detailed report carried out by Edward Llwyd during the early years of the 18th century, but not all of Llwyd's reports have survived, the ones relating to Ceredigion having been lost in the disastrous fire at Hafod in Ceredigion. Jervoise had the habit of starting at the estuary of a river and working his way upstream, naming each bridge in turn. I have found difficulty in locating 60% of the bridges that Jervoise lists, but does not describe in detail. Some, like William Edwards' 'Pontycymer' was demolished almost before his book was published but others, for example the little bridge over Nant Brân near Brecon, still survives more or less in its original condition.

Discovering Bridges

Apart from the examples on private land, all the bridges were accessible when I visited them, although in some cases the position from which they could be viewed was somewhat limited. There was however one rare exception. Old 'Pontardaf' between Cefncoed and Storey Arms in the Brecon Beacons carried the ancient parish road to Penderyn until 1926. When last seen, it was still in reasonably good condition, but the roadway has gone, and someone has helped themselves to large chunks of the parapet stones. During severe drought, the river returns to its original course and meanders through its twin segmental arches. At all other times it is hidden from view under many feet of water, at the bottom of Llwyn-onn reservoir.

A number of bridges on the Landranger and Pathfinder maps are named, and these are listed in the appendix. Many of them are modern concrete constructions that have merely retained the original name or, in the case of small streams passing under a trunk road, are often little more than culverts.

Motorway river crossings can usually be ignored as being far too modern, unless you are an admirer of contemporary bridge building techniques. But even those of us who prefer our bridges to be draped in ivy and crumbling away cannot fail to admire the elegant lines of some of the modern structures. The two that carry the 'Heads of the Valleys' road over Afon Taf Fawr and Afon Taf Fach at Cefncoedycymer near Merthyr Tudful, are worth more than a passing glance, and one of them is the ideal viewing point for the fine railway viaduct just below.

Bridges on trunk roads can be a little more rewarding, although most of the original construction will have been widened or rebuilt long ago. Roads marked on the maps as 'secondary' and 'unclassified' are where the most interesting road bridges are to be found. Any river crossing within a forestry plantation will probably have been culverted either when the planting took place, or when the thinnings were removed. One shudders to think of what happened to 'Pont-Sarnoffeiriad', an ancient clapper bridge destroyed without thought near Dolwyddelan. Thankfully, the number of new plantations are now greatly reduced. Even in other remote hilly areas, where the blanket of green has been kept at bay by the few hill farmers struggling to survive, there could well be further disappointments for the bridge enthusiast. A large number of interesting bridges in upland areas have been destroyed by smashing away the arches, and erecting steel girders across the abutments. This was often done to facilitate the path of heavy lime lorries and agricultural contractors' ploughing equipment onto hills that were previously inaccessible to them.

Most of the bridges described can be reached in a family car, but be warned; the roads are often narrow, with few passing places, and having to reverse back for a hundred yards (100 metres) or more when faced with an oncoming vehicle can be a common occurrence. There are also a few bridges that can only be visited by the hale and hearty, involving an hour or so of hard walking along mountain tracks. 'Pont Llaeron' and 'Pont Sgethin' are two such remote river crossings in Meirionnydd that are well worth visiting. While most of the bridges to be found on trunk roads are modern and, with a few exceptions, of little interest, their construction often resulted in the original bridge being bypassed. A few can still be found, ignored by the local authority who either lack the finance to demolish them, or are enlightened enough to realise their historical interest and allow them to survive. Even a bridge that is no longer in use is still the responsibility of the local Highways Department, who are obliged to ensure the safety of any wheeled vehicle. In order to prevent vehicles from passing over a disused bridge, the approaches are often either obstructed by dumping winter grit or chippings, or by placing bollards across the roadway. An extreme case is the disused rail girder bridge in Cwm Aman in Glamorgan. Here the authorities not only removed a section of the embankment, but bricked up the ends as well. This costly work, carried out to prevent motor cycle maniacs from using it for their stunts, was still cheaper than complete demolition.

Bypassed bridges that are subjected to preservation orders, such as 'Pont-spwdwr' near Cydweli, and 'Pont-Dafydd' in Clwyd, are safe from official destruction but still require protection from less enlightened members of the public who often find them to be an useful source of building material.

Bridges are best viewed from the river bank. In my opinion, downstream is preferable as there is something more satisfying in having the water flowing towards you. The large amount of flood debris caught on the upstream side of piers often makes bridges look unattractive when viewed from that side.

River banks are dangerous places, particularly if you intend to examine underneath a bridge. A dry spell when the water level is low is the best, and stout footwear or rubber boots must be worn. Wet feet are an occupational hazard for the bridge enthusiast. I once came across two men clearing ivy from a listed bridge, one hacking it away with a spade, while his companion supported the ladder in the strong current, dressed in thigh waders.

13

Do not hesitate to chat up the locals. Far from thinking that you are mad, they will only be too pleased that you are taking an interest in their little bit of history. A pub or the village store is often a good place to inquire, particularly if they are kept by someone who has lived in the locality for years. Find out if the bridge has a name, when it was built, and if there are any interesting stories attached to it. Had it not been for local assistance, many of the bridges described here would never have been discovered.

Above all, stand back and marvel at the skills of the rural bridge builders. How they ever managed to span those raging torrents and deep chasms is often beyond belief.

Wooden Bridges

During the Middle Ages, and even as late as the mid 18th century, most of the bridges of rural Wales were constructed of wood. Such crossings were easy to build, often without specialist labour, and easily repaired or replaced when damaged or destroyed by flood. They were the most effective means of crossing where the banks were too steep, or the water too deep, to allow rivers to be forded.

Many of the artists of the period depict such bridges, often neglected and unusable. Even when in reasonable condition, they were a danger to life and limb. A large number of the bridges recorded by Edward Llwyd were made of wood. Only very gradually, as finance and support became more available through local rates and taxes, and the need for more permanent and safer means of crossing rivers, were they replaced by stone constructions.

No wooden bridge of any great age survives in Wales, the well known tourist attraction, the Miners Bridge at Betws-y-coed, being a modern reconstruction. Its only interesting feature is the way it is placed at a sharp angle across the river, to compensate for the higher level of the bank on the far side, causing it to be used rather like a ladder.

There are, however, several wooden bridges still to be found, although they are rapidly being replaced by concrete girder or prefabricated metal types. Most of these will either be footbridges in nature reserves or country parks, or a means of connecting a farm's property on either side of a river.

An interesting wooden bridge used to connect a farmhouse, a little east of Abergynolwyn in Meirionnydd, with a minor road. Built over Afon Dysynni, this much photographed rickety construction of wood planks and piles appeared in several publications, until it was recently replaced by a stronger modern crossing. Further north in Snowdonia, wooden planks resting on rough stone piers can still be found, one of the best known being at Llynnau Mymbyr near Capel Curig.

The hiker, explorer and bridge fanatic will no doubt be aware of other bridges, but a word of warning; many will be on private land and can be unsafe. By all means view them if possible without trespassing, but do not attempt to cross over them. You can hardly expect compensation if it collapses, and an injury is sustained.

One of the major problems in constructing wooden bridges in remote places is that of getting the semi-assembled parts to the site. This problem was solved with the assistance of modern technology when a bridge was required over Nant Llechau in Cwm Nedd (*the Vale of*

Neath), to allow walkers visiting the Henryd falls to complete the round trip. It was assembled miles away and transported in by helicopter.

One of the last wooden bridges of any importance to be replaced by a metal crossing, which has in fact destroyed much of the romance of the spot, is 'Parsons Bridge' above Pontarfynach *(Devils' Bridge)*. George Borrow went out of his way to visit the bridge, which he described as 'a couple of planks and a pole flung over a chasm'. Somehow, I doubt that the old traveller would approve of the new structure.

Suspension Bridges

The principal of suspending a bridge from ropes stretched across a river or a ravine is of great antiquity. The earliest ropes would have probably been made from some type of vegetation. It would have been little more than one rope strung a few feet above the other, and crossing would be undertaken by holding on to the top rope and sliding the feet along the bottom one.

Only the armed forces, during training session, need to carry out this perilous technique these days. Explorers to the remotest regions of the world can expect to find that even the poorest countries have upgraded their suspension bridges to include two guide ropes, and some form of plank roadway.

It may come as something of a surprise to learn that bridges of the more primitive type were to be found in remote parts of Wales until quite recently. These were sometimes called swing, or pendant bridges. The former name is now restricted to a particular type of canal bridge that swings open, whilst the latter is no longer used to describe a crossing.

A very crude version, as postcard pictures confirm, was to be found at Aberaeron in Dyfed, where it was known locally as *Lovers Bridge*. I have been unable to determine whether young men crossed it to impress their loved ones, or whether anyone foolhardy enough to attempt it was considered to be madly in love.

The genius of Thomas Telford has provided Wales with two fine suspension bridges. Most of the visitors to north Wales will be aware of the masterpieces of engineering at Conwy and over the Menai Straights. Until the Cleddau and Severn bridges were built in recent times, they dominated the suspension bridge technique in Wales for so long that all other similar crossings were minuscule by comparison.

Most other examples of suspension bridges are to be found over wider rivers, serving small communities either as a footbridge or being suitable only for light traffic.

There is a fine 1920s type over Afon Gwy *(Wye)* at Llansteffan, and another with interesting features at Llangollen. I can recall seeing one connecting Pentre-Elan *(Elan Village)* with the main road, but have been unable to examine it due to access difficulties, and circumstances were similar with another bridge over Afon Wysg *(the Usk)*.

Some of the most recent constructions are over Afon Seiont near Caernarfon Castle, and another that carries the footpath from Merthyr Mawr to Ogwr *(Ogmore)* in the Vale of Glamorgan. The latter must be

17

one of the most expensive means of taking a footpath over a river, since those using it are often unable to complete the journey due to the stepping stones, opposite the castle, being under water.

In the 1840s, one Philip Thomas of Pontypridd built a suspension bridge at Llanymddyfri *(Llandovery)*, inspired by the Menai Bridge. Little is known about its short life span, and it was replaced by a more conventional crossing before the end of the century.

A suspension bridge of particular interest is the one that links Ynys Lawd *(South Stack)* lighthouse to Ynys Gybi *(Holyhead Island)* and the rest of Ynys Môn. According to Thomas Roscoe it was built in 1827, and although there have been some inevitable repairs, it still serves as a footbridge.

Floods

The Highways Act passed in 1555 should have solved the problem of bridge maintenance, when it provided the County Quarter Sessions with the power to levy rates for their repair. But it was some considerable time before the Act made any impression on the most remote parts of Wales. A traveller in the 17th century described the roads in Maldwyn *(Montgomeryshire)* as the worst he had ever seen, and there is no reason to believe that the bridges were in any better condition.

From the early medieval period churches and monasteries had taken the responsibility for building and maintaining bridges. Some of the earliest bridges in north Wales, those at Rhuddlan and Llangollen, were sponsored by the bishop of St Asaph, and at one time his coat of arms appeared on a plaque built into the parapet.

After the dissolution of the monasteries the local gentry took over bridge building and maintenance, often collecting contributions among their friends to finance the work.

Gradually the County took over the responsibility, whilst some parishes were able to call on all able bodied men to spend a number of days, without payment, on road and bridge maintenance. According to the reports of various Quarter Sessions throughout Wales, most counties were having difficulty financing even the repairs to the poor timber bridges under their control, while the parishes were often reluctant to levy extra rates on the community, although some could be reclaimed from the County in some areas.

The following excerpts from the records of the Montgomeryshire Court of Great Sessions give some indication of the condition of the counties bridges towards the end of the 17th century.

1680, Pont Rhiwgar and Pont Garneddwen, ruinous and decayed.
1680, Ye bridge at Caersoose in disrepair.
1681, Pont Sycoed, out of repair.

The situation was no better elsewhere, as Brecknock Sessions reported that in 1686 Pont Felin-fach was 'out of repair', and again in 1689. There is little doubt that the main reason for these failures was a lack of repair and flood damage. Even as early as 1535, Leyland had reported that: 'Usk bridge at Breckon was thrown down by the range of Usk water'. The problem was widespread on all the larger rivers, with Brecknock Quarter Sessions being informed again in 1691 that 'Pont Newydd over the Usk was ruinated and carried away by flood'.

Even stone bridges were vulnerable. Not one above Rhaeadr on Afon Gwy (*Wye*) survived the floods of 1880.

Some of the crossings that suffered more than most were the ill-fated bridges built over Afon Gwy at Glasbury. In 1311 there was only a ferry over Afon Gwy (*The Wye*) there. A bridge that was built in 1665 was washed away; another built in 1738 suffered the same fate. In 1777 William Edwards built a fine five arch bridge there, his only contract in mid-Wales, but even the work of the master was not strong enough to withstand the ravages of Afon Gwy in full spate, and the bridge collapsed during the severe floods of 1795.

Lofty, single arch bridges, built on solid foundations were the most likely to survive floodwaters, but these were restricted to narrower rivers. The more numerous the piers, the more suspectable the bridge to flood damage. Debris would gather around the cutwaters and abutments, causing a damming effect and putting greater pressure on the piers. In some cases large trees being swept downstream acted as battering rams, and if the water level was high enough, the arch was often swept away.

In a valley with low lying banks and a wide flood plane, water would undermine the abutments, resulting in the collapse of the entire structure. The construction of land arches, which would let the flood water through, was an effective but expensive means of easing the problem.

Pont Walton in Dyffryn Dyfi, a concrete bridge built in 1926 was destroyed in this manner in 1964, and at the same time floating trees struck the lattice girder 'Jubilee bridge' a little downstream, pushing it off its abutments. This left the valley with only one serviceable bridge, the narrow 18th century arch at Mallwyd, in a twelve mile length of river.

In 1831 Pont Caerfyrddin (*Carmarthen Bridge*) was in danger of collapsing due to the pressure of water building up against the arches, and a wall was removed to increase the waterway which saved the bridge.

The flooding of low lying areas would cause delays of days or even a week or more in some valleys, one of the worst hit stretches being between Pontarddyfi and the town of Machynlleth. This took place with frustrating regularity until the road level was raised in the 1950s. There were attempts to raise the river banks by dumping quarry waste at the weakest points, but this allowed the flood-waters to raise to parapet height on the bridge, putting it in considerable danger, and the obstructions had to be removed. The Dyfi still floods regularly at this point, forcing a twelve mile detour for most small vehicles.

For a period of many years, before stone bridges of a more substantial nature were built in the early 1800s, the Counties preferred to make do with wooden structures. They took for granted that they would be washed away regularly most winters, but could be re-erected quickly and fairly cheaply each summer without the need to employ the specialist labour required for stone bridges.

However inconvenient the loss of a bridge was to a community, only part of the structure would often collapse and it could still be used with care. Part of the pier of the bridge at Llandeilo Rwnws on Afon Tywi had been washed away when Jervoise inspected it in 1931, but according to him 'owing to the excellence of the masonry the arches stood firm', and the bridge was repaired. It proved that a once and for all investment in a solid construction was worthwhile, but the cost of building such a bridge put a severe strain on the local economy.

As the economy of rural Wales began to improve, the Counties were able to finance their bridge building and repairs. Brecknock Sessions reported in 1823 that 'Pont Abergwerndwr' was rebuilt in stone, as was 'Pont Sor'. The Anglesey Sessions did not have to contend with such wild rivers, but also appeared to have more cash to spare. As early as 1769 they ordered that 'Rhydgarland Bridge and Pont y Foryd be immediately well and sufficiently repaired'.

Rivers in full flood are dangerous places and loss of life resulting in the collapse of a bridge has occurred, although few such accidents appear in the record books. Thomas Pennant informs us in *Tours of Wales*, that 'while a man was leaning over the battlements of 'Pont Halkyn' it unfortunately gave way where by he was drowned'. Five of the builders of Pont Llandeilo were lucky to escape with their lives when the timbers were washed away while they were working on it in 1840. They were dragged half drowned from the river some distance downstream.

One of the best documented disasters involving a collapsed bridge was the one at Caerleon Bridge on a wet and windy October night in 1779, when the centre of the wooden structure collapsed in floodwater. At the time a certain Mrs Williams was crossing the bridge on her way to collect her husband from a local pub where he had spent several hours, and she felt he might require assistance to get home. The local inhabitants, on hearing cries, came out of their homes, and saw her being carried downstream clinging to the wreckage, and were convinced that she would be drowned. Being a level headed woman she did not panic, and clung on as far as Newport Bridge. She attempted to climb on to the piers here but the force of the water was too great and it smashed the timbers onto which she was clinging, leaving her with only a few small bits to support her as she was swept out towards the estuary. Her faint cries were heard by the crew of a small vessel, who gave chase, and after much difficulty managed to pull her abroad. The next morning she was taken to the mayor of Newport, who sent her back to Caerleon in a specially hired coach. She was in good physical condition despite her ordeal, and lived to a ripe old age.

Not everyone was as lucky as Mrs Williams, and the young child who fell from the Corris Railway Bridge near Machynlleth in 1947 was drowned.

Modern bridges are still vulnerable to flood damage. The collapse of the Glanrhyd rail bridge over Afon Tywi, which resulted in the loss of several lives, was a severe reminder of the terrible strength of a river in full spate.

Failures

The best known construction failure was the one that befell William Edwards during his attempts to build the massive stone arch of his second bridge at Pontypridd. His first bridge, of three stone arches, was washed away in 1743, two years after completion. Edwards had given assurance that it would last for seven years and, in order to avoid the same mishap again, he decided to attempt a single wide arch, well above the raging Afon Taf. The hundred of Senghennydd, commissioners of the original bridge, were sceptical of this attempt, which was to be the longest single span in Britain at that time. But work commenced despite the adverse publicity, and was almost completed by November 1745 when another flood washed away the timber supports, and the arch collapsed. A report in the *Gentleman's Magazine* of that year describes the disaster:

> The rivers in this county have lately been very heavy and the flood have carried away an arch built over the river Taff, a hundred and forty four feet wide, and said to be the widest in Europe.

An account published in the 'Annual Register' for 1764, does not record the actual amount of damage caused to the arch by the collapse of the timbering, but one is led to believe that only a small portion of the arch collapsed. Work began at once to rebuild the bridge using stronger supports, and this time it was completed successfully.

The critical point of arch construction was the 'knocking out of the centre', as the removal of the supports was known. In many cases this resulted in the arch twisting, and in the event of bad building techniques, often its entire collapse. Edwards' great arch survived this critical operation, but further disaster was to strike.

There are conflicting reports regarding the time that William Edwards' second bridge stood, ranging from six weeks to one year. Tillotson, in his book *The Picturesque Scenery of Wales* (1860), states that the arch collapsed before the parapets were built in 1751. Whatever the time factor, the fact that William Edwards was unfamiliar with this method of construction was obvious. According to the 'Annual Register' report:

> He was no master of the rules of architecture, and did not understand the necessity of preserving the equilibrium.

The builder was not an architect, but rather a country contractor risking a very ambitious project that no well known architect had hitherto attempted, which makes the above criticism a little rich. But the second collapse of the arch had a profound effect on Edwards. Having successfully 'knocked the centres out', to suffer a later failure was a bitter disappointment.

The bridge collapsed due to the weight of the abutments pushing the keystones upwards, and out of position. This was a major problem with long arch constructions, and no doubt there were others built on a smaller scale that suffered the same mishap. In order to make the ascent, to the centre of the bridge from either direction, as easy as possible, the approaches were constructed to carry a great deal of material in order to raise the roadway to an acceptable level, but putting a great deal of weight on the abutments.

The third attempt to build the bridge only came about when the local gentry, impressed by William Edwards' innovative idea and his standing in the community, carried out a collection to enable him to clear some of his debts and proceed with another attempt. The materials were still at the site, although at the bottom of the river. It was the willingness of his labour force to 'work without wages as long as we can buy bread for ourselves and families', that allowed the work to continue. According to the 'Annual Register', the third attempt was successful for the following reasons:

In order to lessen the quantity of matter in the abutments pressing on the crown he has constructed three circular arches in the abutments; these pass through from side to side, and gradually decrease in the ascent.

There are reports that William Edwards obtained the solution of using the openings in the haunches of the bridge from a passer by, possibly a soldier, who had seen such work carried out abroad. It was a complete success, and soon became the standard practice in long arch construction, and was used by him in a number of his later bridges. The date of the completion of the third arch is given as 1755, but this could well have been a year or two out.

The success of the third bridge, in spite of all the odds, gave rise to the Welsh saying 'Tri Chynnig i Gymro' *(Three Attempts for a Welshman)*. This is still often heard when the first, or even the second attempts at anything, goes wrong. The construction of the bridge, and the life of William Edwards, is well documented by H.P. Richards in his informative booklet, *William Edwards, Architect, Builder, Minister.*

Other notable failures that have been recorded are that of Pont Llandeilo, which collapsed in 1846 when 'part of the centre was carried off' during building, again due to floodwater moving the timber

24

supports. It is very probable that a number of bridges suffered building failures, but history only records the most spectacular.

It is known that Pont Rhydlanfair over the Conwy was only erected at the third attempt, after earlier efforts by another builder had failed. There is much documentation regarding the collapse of 'Overton Bridge' on Afon Dyfrdwy *(the Dee)* when it was being built in 1812. Not only did this catastrophe involve the Counties of Flintshire and Denbighshire in a great deal of unnecessary expense, it also cost the builder Thomas Penson, Senior, his post as County Surveyor.

There had been bridges crossing the Dee at this point for a long time, the earlier ones being of wood. The first stone bridge built during the 18th Century suffered many problems and costly repairs, and in 1810 the two counties that shared the border decided to build a new bridge. Thomas Penson, Senior, had been appointed surveyor in 1806 at a salary of one hundred and five pounds per annum. His contract included a restrictive clause which could well have been the deciding factor in the events that were to follow. It stated that any estimates he gave had to be:

'the same or less than any other person who offers to undertake the work.'

Penson's estimate for the new bridge was 5,200 pounds, a sum that left him with little to spare for emergencies. To make matters worse, the magistrates refused his application to erect a toll gate and house on the bridge, by which he hoped to recoup some of the money spent in the construction.

Once again it was the building of a single stone arch that was the root of the problem. By 1812 almost all of the estimated money had been used, and only the approaches and abutments completed. Faced with the likelihood of being over budget, and with no means of recouping his losses, Penson began to cut corners on such a scale that the authorities began to have serious doubts about the contract, and suggested that 'an eminent architect' should be employed to check on the construction work.

Penson was ordered to draw up new plans for a bridge with an iron arch, and also one of wood (as a last resort), and make them available to William Hazeldine, who was producing much of the iron work for the Chirk and Pontcysylltau aqueducts.

The magistrates, who had ultimate responsibility over the contract, relented. Although they had serious doubts about the condition of the slender stone arch, they allowed work to continue. Their concern was well founded for on August 13th, 1813 the partly completed arch collapsed.

During the next two years Penson was in constant conflict with his employers over plans for a new bridge. He had been ordered to submit new plans once again, this time for a bridge of two stone arches, but had failed to do so. He was discharged from his post in early 1815, but during his difficult time with the Flintshire authority, he had managed to gain the respect of the neighbouring County, and was eventually employed by them.

The contract was handed over to his son Thomas Penson, Junior, who completed the new two arched bridge in 1816. Penson Junior was later to become surveyor of Trefaldwyn (*Montgomeryshire*), where he successfully completed a number of bridge constructions.

The other notable collapsed arch was that of the Porthceri Viaduct in Barry, where the blame was placed on the poor foundations and materials that were used for one of the piers. This occurred after the line was opened and caused considerable inconvenience to the Barry Railway Company, who had to build a temporary line while repairs were undertaken.

The highest number of aqueduct failures occurred on the stretch of the Montgomery canal, when all of the five crossings, including the major ones over Afon Rhiw and Afon Efyrnwy, either completely or partly collapsed. Two were later replaced with iron troughs, but the two at Rhiw and over Afon Efyrnwy had to be rebuilt.

The reasons for these misfortunes are well documented by Stephen Hughes in his *Archaeology of the Montgomery Canal*, and are given as insufficient foundations to bear the weight of the puddling clay type of trough, and on the inexperience of its builder, John Dartford. Dartford, like Penson, paid the price for his failure, and in 1796 resigned his many canal contracts and fled to America, leaving others the thankless task of trying to rectify his mistakes.

It is worth noting that even present day building methods, with all the technological advancements, are not immune to failure, as the builders of Pont Cleddau found out to their cost when some of the concrete piers collapsed mysteriously during construction.

The main causes of disasters have been, without doubt, floods and construction failures, but there were instances that were caused by freak accidents. It is well known that Pont Britannia had its wooden linings destroyed by fire in 1970. What is less well known is that a part of the railway viaduct at Risca, one of the longest in Wales, was blown down in a gale early this century.

Pont Brittania was not the only bridge to be destroyed by fire. In May 1848, the 1300 foot long Newport Viaduct over Afon Wysg (*Usk*) was totally destroyed when a worker, inserting a red hot bolt, started a fire that got out of control.

Names

At some time or other during their lifespan, most bridges have been given a name. During the time when maps were inadequate, and unavailable to anyone other than the rich, it became important to be able to identify a particular river crossing. Pont Pedair Onnen *(Four Ashes Trees Bridge)* was an example of when a landmark would be used to enable strangers to locate its position. The number of towns and villages that have the prefix 'PONT' to their name, would suggest that they developed around a river crossing. Two that have grown into large communities, and still have the Welsh prefix, are Pontypridd and Pont-y-pŵl.

Very few have taken to using the English translation, Bridgend and Cowbridge being the most obvious; but the original names of Pen-y-bont ar Ogwr and Y Bont-faen are still used by Welsh speakers, and can be seen on bilingual road signs. It is perhaps surprising that the largely anglicized county of Gwent has retained the original Welsh names of its bridges.

Before bridges became permanent features, which only came about when they were strong enough to withstand the winter floods, rivers would be crossed by fording, and the Welsh name 'Rhyd' is apparent in many place-names. Bridges built over, or near, such fords would be named after it: Pont-rhyd-y-fen, Pont-rhyd-y-groes and its tongue twister of a neighbour Pontrhydfendigaid, being the best known. In areas that did not develop into settlements, bridges often took the name of the rivers they crossed, and there are several such names on the O.S. maps, for example Pont ar Afon Gam in Trefaldwyn. Others that crossed near the confluence of two rivers were named after the area – Pont Abergeirw and Pont Aberbrân, being only two of many.

It was inevitable that the English word 'Bridge' should take precedence in some localities where the Welsh language was in decline, such as Glamorgan and south Pembrokeshire. Here we find such names as Lechwith Bridge, Merlins Bridge, and Cannaston Bridge, but they are in the minority. Many of the original Welsh names were particularly beautiful, and those fluent in the language will relish the names that defy translation and roll sweetly off the tongue, such as Pontpenchwiban, Pontwedws, and Pontywrisgen.

All the bridges were built by someone who may, or may not, have received credit for his efforts in the form of a plaque. In a few cases, the grateful community would name a bridge after its creator. The one at Llansannan in Conwy was built by one 'Blythin Lloyd', and was promptly named after him. Also in north-eastern Conwy is the longest name I have come across; Pont Edward Sion ap Dafydd:

Bridges with English sounding names pay tribute to the benefactor who provided the money to build them, such as 'Pont Henri', which is also the name of the small township. In one case the original name was changed when someone, probably the local squire, came along and replaced an earlier bridge with a more substantial structure, which resulted in Pontarddwyryd finding itself named Pont Baker.

We are indebted to the early travellers for recording many of the names of bridges that have long since disappeared, although the original name has been retained by the new structure. Leyland, as early as the 16th century, noted many names, but it was Edward Llwyd, a hundred and fifty years later, who carried out the most accurate survey.

Those who have read his accounts may consider the language quaint or even picturesque, but it makes it almost impossible in some instances to find the correct Welsh word. Pont Blythin was noted as 'Pont Bleddyb', and Pontcefncestyll cause no end of problems when it appeared as 'Pont Keven Kestlith'.

Bridge names were changed for a variety of reasons. Pont Ffinant near Dinas Mawddwy crossed Afon Dyfi near the stream that was the natural boundary between medieval southern Gwynedd, and northern Powys. The name was retained as recently as the 19th century, when it starts appearing as Pont Minllyn, since it is in the hamlet of Minllyn. Other bridge names were changed to facilitate the early travellers, now known as tourists; for example, the lilting but hardly difficult Pontarfynach was changed to the well known Devil's Bridge.

The oddly named Pont y Pump in the village of Llangrannog in Ceredigion is so named because five builders participated in its construction, and left their initials on the parapet. But some bridges have names that seem to defy any reasonable attempt to discover their origins. What could be the history behind bridges called Pontyblew *(Bridge of the Hairs)*, Pontycame *(Bridge of Footsteps)*, or the mysterious Pont Ysgaden *(Herring Bridge)* which is deep in land-locked mid-Wales.

It is interesting to note that aqueducts are named after the river they span or the area nearest to them, and railway bridges, with the exception of large viaducts, remain nameless. One notable exception to this rule is Pont Gethin in Glyn Lledr *(Valley)*, named after Gethin Jones, who also built Betws-y-coed railway station.

New bridges were regularly built once building techniques improved enough for them to become permanent features. Some retained the name of their wooden predecessors, others were renamed, but many were just called New Bridge, which is probably the most widespread name one can expect to find. When a community took roots around a new bridge, such as the one over Afon Ebbw in Gwent, and took its name from the bridge, there were no problems of identification. But later places with similar intentions had to have more detail added, hence the name 'Newbridge on Wye', and 'Newbridge on Usk'.

It is unusual to find a bridge named after its main user, rather than the builder or sponsor, but this was the case with Pont yr Offeiriad *(Parsons' Bridge)*, over Afon Mynach near Pontarfynach. The present modern structure is of little interest, but the original crude wooden crossing was used by a member of the clergy to visit his flock, among them a group of lead miners, on the other side of the raging river. Bridges that lead somewhere can act as a signpost; Pont y Gwaith Haearn *(Bridge to the Ironworks)* needs no explanation.

It was common practice to charge to cross bridges erected on private land, and later during the turnpike era. It is however most unusual to come across a name which is based on the amount of toll paid. The small hamlet of Pennybridge near Pembroke appears to be the only one in Wales.

Repairs and Restoration

Before the beginning of the 18th century there were very few wheeled vehicles on the roads of rural Wales, which were hard baked ruts in summer and an impassable quagmire in winter. It was well into the middle of the 19th century before the Turnpike Trusts began to make any realistic headway in improving the roads, and this was reflected in the condition of the bridges.

The few stone bridges were intended for packhorses, and were seldom more than a couple of yards wide. Only one person leading an animal could cross at a time. With no formal means of controlling the users, few though they were, serious problems could occur if one or the other refused to give way. J.G. Wood, in the early 19th century, reports that Pont Sygyn near Beddgelert was 'wide enough for the passage of a horse'. Even larger bridges near big towns were seldom wide enough to take a carriage, as G. Rees states in 1819 that Pont Llandeilo was 'so narrow a carriage cannot be passed upon it without some danger'. Gradually the influence of the Turnpike Trusts began to result in some improvements, but their finances were frequently insecure. Many went into liquidation, leaving others to collect the tolls, but spending only a small proportion of the money raised on road improvements.

There were considerable objections to paying the tolls, which led to the so called 'Rebecca Riots' breaking out in south-western Wales. The drovers, some of the main road users, would travel miles to avoid a toll gate, whilst other invented ingenious ways to avoid at least part of the payment. With a tax on each wheel, one crafty haulier designed a three-wheeled cart.

Improvements were therefore slow, and it was only the main coaching routes that benefitted at first. Even then, improvements to roads were hindered by the condition of the bridges, which were still often under the control of the parish or the County, who could not afford to repair them. One of the main complaints was that the local community seldom benefitted from the improvements.

To demolish a bridge and rebuild another at the same place would cause serious disruption while the work was taking place, which explains why so many 'new' bridges were constructed a little up or downstream of the original. If a stone bridge was established the acceptable method of improvement was to widen it, usually on the upstream side. This was the side most prone to flood damage, and doubling the width not only made it wide enough to allow coaches and carts to pass each other, but in effect also provided a new bridge at half the cost. Theophilus Jones states that

Brecon Bridge was widened in 1794 and that 'two waggons may now with ease repass one another'.

As the traffic increased and generally became larger and wider, even further widening became necessary. The second widening would take place on the downstream side, which resulted in the old structure being sandwiched in the middle of the new stonework. One bridge to receive such an improvement was the one built by William Edwards at Usk, and in later years other bridges on main roads were improved in the same manner.

A bridge, now sadly demolished, where this type of repair work was much in evidence, was the one at Glantwymyn in the Dyfi valley. It was described by Jervoise in 1931 as 'when viewed from the river level appears to consist of three bridges built side by side'. He goes on to say that the original structure was about five feet wide and the two later additions about eight feet each in width.

A problem that often faced coaches and heavily laden wagons was having to negotiate the high 'hump' of a single arch bridge. In many cases passengers had to alight, a common enough practice in hilly areas anyway. Chains were fixed to the rear of the vehicle, as well as drags on the wheels, in order to prevent it running out of control down the far side. Until the roadway of William Edwards' bridge at Pontypridd was replaced by steps in the 1920s, the groves cut by the chains were still visible on the crown of the bridge.

In order to lessen the steep rise over some bridges, long single arch construction being the most obvious, the roadway was raised at the approaches. This was done at Pontypridd, but was a risky venture as too much weight on the haunches could dislodge the keystones, resulting in the collapse of the arch.

It will be apparent to the bridge enthusiast that the high arches were placed well above the height required to avoid floodwater, and were in fact constructed in such a way so as to allow the builder to obtain the correct arch geometry resulting in a perfect segment.

Although the Counties, and to a lesser degree the parishes were responsible for bridge construction and repairs in most areas by the beginning of the 19th century, a few local businessmen and landowners continued to sponsor their own. It was not unknown for the County to render assistance to a landlord who, having met with some financial crisis, could not complete a bridge he had started building. A plaque on the bridge at Merthyr Mawr near Pen-y-bont ar Ogwr *(Bridgend)* states that it was started by Edward Nichol, but was completed by the County.

Many poor parishes had difficulty raising enough money to maintain their roads and bridges. One of the 1809 Quarter Sessions at Dolgellau took the unusual step of fining the inhabitants of the parish of Ffestiniog fifty pounds for failing to maintain its roads. It appeared to have little effect, for the parish was again fined the following year, but some effort must have been made as the penalty was reduced to seventeen pounds.

At the time the slate quarries were developing in the area, and the owners were anxious to improve the roads and bridges to facilitate the transportation of their products. Some were prepared to meet the cost themselves on the condition that some relief was forthcoming in the form of exemption from rates and local taxes.

In 1822 an agreement was reached between the parish and one of the owners, Samuel Holland, concerning the construction of a bridge and a section of road. As a result, Holland agreed to be responsible for all the cost of buying the land, all the legal costs, the cost of constructing the road and bridge, and to maintain them in good condition for a period of three years. During this time his quarry at Rhiwbryfdir was to be free of all rates and taxes. At the end of the three years the road and bridge was to be taken over by the parish. The work was completed in 1825, and taken over as agreed in 1828.

Bridges that spanned rivers forming the county boundary were in a position to have the repair costs shared between the two authorities. The plaque on Builth Wells Bridge, and also the one at Felin Cwrws near Henllan in Dyfed confirms this alliance of sharing costs. The sharing of building costs was only feasible when both Counties could agree on the type of structure needed, and had the necessary finance to carry out the work. When William Edwards' fine stone bridge over the Wye at Glasbury was washed away in the flood of 1795, less than twenty years after it was completed, the two counties of Brecknock and Radnor could not agree on the type of replacement. As a result the Brecknock side was repaired in stone, but for many years the Radnor half remained a rickety wooden structure. The same situation applied to Chepstow Bridge, as depicted in an illustration by Richard Colt Hoarse, which can be seen at the National Library of Wales.

The period between 1840 and the turn of the century saw major repairs taking place, including the widening and reconstruction of many of the older stone bridges. New structures were also built, often bypassing earlier bridges of considerable interest. Building on this scale was a costly business and having managed to build a bridge, the County still had to find the means of protecting it against the ravages of flood and general wear and tear. In 1819, the cost of erecting a stone bridge over Afon Tywi at Llangadog was shared by the parishes of Llandeilo,

Llansadwrn, Llanddeusant, and Myddfai.

Charging a toll on those using bridges to pay for its erection and maintenance dates as far back as the late 1700s. A bridge was built over Afon Tywi at Dryslwyn to satisfy a local request by farmers carting lime, but they found themselves having to pay a penny to cross on weekdays, and two pence on Sunday. One feels that the Lords Day Observance Society had some involvement there. Pedestrians were allowed to return on just the one payment, a practice still used until recently at Barmouth Bridge.

In cases where insufficient money was available to build a bridge, funds were borrowed from the rates and repaid from tolls levied on its users. This method was used when a one thousand pound loan was allowed to enable Phylip Thomas of Pontypridd to build his suspension bridge at Llanymddyfri in the 1840s. No mention is made of the interest charged, and one wonders if this short lived construction ever took enough in tolls to recoup the cost of building.

The parish of Llanymddyfri had great difficulty in finding suitable persons to contract for the repair of their bridges. In 1764 two people agreed to maintain the bridge over Afon Tywi for a staggering twenty-one years at five shillings (25p) annually, which included supplying the materials! The contract, not surprisingly, was a disaster, and that particular bridge deteriorated so much that a new one had to be built by Thomas Edwards (William's son) in 1773 for eight thousand pounds. In 1786, one Evan Rees contracted to repair all the bridges in the parish for a period of five years, free of charge, in return for being allowed to hold all the parish meetings at his public house. The deal appears to have been a most satisfactory one from his point of view, which only goes to prove the revenue that can be obtained from thirsty councillors. How much of it actually went on bridge maintenance was not recorded.

The County Quarter Sessions would allocate contracts for the repairs of bridges under their control, and work would normally be undertaken by a small gang of masons working as a team, or by a family concern. Small bridges would often be contracted to one man, but even in those days the cut and thrust of business was very apparent. Once a quote had been presented to one meeting, it often happened that someone else would have undercut it by the time the decision to award the contract had been taken. In 1765 two Dolgellau masons, John Richard and Gruffydd Richard offered to rebuild Bont Newydd with 'two arches, battlements, pavements, and key', for two hundred pounds. No decision was taken on their quote during the meeting, and by the time the Sessions met again a month later they had been undercut by two other

34

masons who agreed to carry out the work for one hundred and five pounds. Both parties had agreed to maintain the bridge for a further fifteen years, but the contract went to the lowest bidder on the condition that they assured the distance between the battlements would be eight feet (2.4 metres).

In some cases the contractor would misunderstand the terms of contract, and would be forced to approach 'someone in authority' to appeal to the Sessions on his behalf to be released from his commitment. There were instances of yeomen farmers putting in bids to repair bridges, when they had no experience of the work, as a means of supplementing their income. Some contracts were awarded· to such persons, possibly due to some form of bribery and corruption, but they usually ended in disaster.

From the early part of the 20th century ferroconcrete bridges were being built, rather than repairing the older stone structures. One of the last stone bridges to be built in the traditional manner was Pont Gwanas near Dolgellau. Completed in 1936, it was duly opened by Herbert Morrison, the then Minister of Transport.

The County Quarter Sessions Reports abound with accounts of bridge repairs. This excerpt was taken from the Meirionnydd Reports, and relates to repairs to Dolymoch bridge in 1748.

Thomas Evan, masons account for repairing Dolymoch, otherwise known as Pontrhydyryrryd Bridge.

Paid for timber for repair the foundations of said bridge
the sum of   1 10 0.
To Thomas Evan, chief mason for twelve days work,   18 0.
To Richard Evan, mason, for eight days work,   8 0.
For carriage of timber,   10 0.
To John Hugh the chief carpenter for twelve days work,   18 0.
To another carpenter for twelve days work,   12 0.
For carriage of stone   4 0.
                                    Total   5 0 0.

Receved July 18th 1748 of Robert Gryffydh esquire the above sum of five pounds in full of all demands for repairing the above bridge mentioned by me.

Thomas Evan.
Witness, Robert Lloyd.

Illustrations

It is not my intention to record all the artists who have painted Welsh bridges, or to comment on their work. The following is only a brief synopsis of some of the best known, and their importance to the bridge historian.

Sir Richard Colt Hoare travelled in Wales during the summers between 1793 and 1813. He visited almost every part of the country, including most large towns of importance. His journals were published in parts at the time, and have appeared in an edited version since. They are somewhat inward looking, containing the inevitable comments about the weather and the bad state of the roads, but provide little insight into life in Wales during those hard times.

Colt Hoare lived in Stourhead in Dorset. He was a man of some means, having gained his wealth from his family's banking business. Wales became his summer destination when travelling in Europe became imprudent on account of the aftermath of the French Revolution. He was impressed, and built himself a summer house at Bala which he used as a base during his travels.

Unlike Pennant who rode, and Borrow who walked, Colt Hoare travelled wherever possible in a hired chaise. Only when the roads became too bad did he resort to riding a horse.

He was a prolific and reasonably talented artist, and most of his sketches and pen and ink drawings have survived. During his visits to Wales he produced well over a hundred, many of which are now in the care of the National Library at Aberystwyth. His drawings illustrated his own journals, as well as those of some of his fellow travellers, notably Richard Fenton.

Some were copied at a later date by engravers and produced as prints. From the bridge historians point of view, three of these are of particular importance. The print of the old bridge at Haverfordwest before it was rebuilt is a particularly fine illustration, as is the one of Newport bridge under construction. He also produced a drawing of Chepstow bridge when it had wooden piers on one side, a stone construction on the other, and a gatehouse in the middle. Among his pen and ink drawings are one of the Chirk viaduct during its construction, and Pont Talybont over Afon Ogwen in Snowdonia.

Had Sir Richard shown the same interest in the many bridges he crossed as he showed in ecclesiastical ruins, then his journals would have provided more valuable information.

Apart from the travellers who toured purely for pleasure and just happened to be talented artists, there were also the professional illustrators who came to sketch and paint. Their work was later sold on merit, or was copied and engraved to feature in some of the many travel books of the period.

The Victorian artist had an obsession for ivy clad ruins, be they castles, churches or bridges, but a close study of a picture that is predominantly of a bridge can yield useful information. Illustrations can sometimes be misleading, for adding or removing the odd arch was a fairly common occurrence, if it made more artistic sense. Less common, but not unknown, was the practice of adding a non-existent bridge, as can be seen in Gastineau's sketch of the Berw cataract on Afon Taf. This could be a case of Gastineau moving a bridge to place it in a more picturesque spot. There are also doubts whether the bridge in his general view of Dolgellau is actually the original Bont-fawr, or rather Pont Llanelltyd from a mile or two away.

Henry Gastineau came to Wales in 1828, and toured under what must have been difficult conditions, carrying his artists materials with him on horseback. He was a prolific artist, and it has been suggested that this was because he was the father of a number of unmarried daughters. This was not a happy position for a struggling artist, creating a work philosophy that was geared towards quantity rather than quality.

Much of his work was in the form of steel engravings, and writers used them to illustrate their books long after Gastineau's visits. J.C. Tillotson's *Picturesque Scenery of Wales*, published some thirty years later, contained many of his illustrations. Gastineau's collected work of Wales was published following his journeys as *Wales Illustrated*, and was widely sold. His prints are still very collectable. Prints of bridges to look out for are Pontcysylltau, Pont Llanrwst, Pont-y-Pair (Betws-y-coed) and Pont Aberteifi. General views of Holt and St Asaph also include bridges.

Another talented artist was W.H. Bartlet. He travelled widely, and his Welsh collection includes only thirteen prints in total, three of which depict bridges. These are of Conwy Castle, Pont Menai, and the suspension bridge linking Ynys Lawd (*South Stack*) to Ynys Gybi (*Holy Island*). The latter is of particular importance as it shows in some detail the anchorage points secured to the rocks below.

The most illustrated bridge, without doubt, is the one at Pontypridd. The erection of an iron bridge alongside it, in 1857, ruined the romantic scene that had attracted some of the best artists of the day to the banks of Afon Taf. A Mr and Mrs Hall, visiting shortly afterwards, instructed their accompanying illustrator to paint the bridge without the offending monstrosity. They referred to the building of this iron bridge, so close to

Edwards' masterpiece, as 'wanton damage'. The illustration that appears in their book is an earlier one, indicating that their illustrator failed to complete his work to a satisfactory degree. Some of the best paintings or sketches of the bridge at Pontypridd are by: Richard Wilson (1767), Paul Sandby (1774), M.A. Rocker (1790), J. Laporte (1804), S. Sands (1819) and Henry Gastineau (1833). The bridge featured on Nantgarw chinaware, and there was a special illustration for a dinner service for the Czar of Russia which is now in the Hermitage in St Petersburg. The bridge at Pontypridd has been depicted in etchings, line engravings, aquatints, lithographs, drawings, water colours and oil paintings. There are about forty in the National Library of Wales in Aberystwyth, and fifteen in the National Museum in Cardiff.

Travellers

During the research of this book, I relied heavily on the works of those who had trampled the highways and byways of Wales long before me. Gerallt Gymro *(Giraldus Cambrensis)* was the first, in 1188, and not surprisingly he had little to offer in the way of information on bridges. Some three and a half centuries later John Leyland was much more helpful. John Leyland (1506-1552) had been appointed the Kings Antiquary, with instructions to visit churches, libraries and similar places to record as many objects of value as he could find. Most of these had been secreted away following the dissolution of the monasteries, and the King was anxious to discover the whereabouts of many of the nations treasures. The task took Leyland about six years, spending some two years in Wales from around 1539-41. During this time he travelled widely, mostly on horseback, the roads being hardly fit for any form of wheeled vehicle. His references to bridges were not great, but the lack of them hindered his movement as he records that; 'There is no bridge on the Wye from Hereford to Builth.'

When he did come across a bridge, he would record its name and position. His spelling of Welsh place-names was probably worse than all the others that were to follow him, and his locations somewhat uncertain. But he did leave us with some indication of the position of crossings at that time.

He records a 'bridge of tymbre 8 miles above Neath Town at Regas'. The bridge was in fact at Resolfen, and not 8 miles from Neath. He did find another 'bridge of tymbre' at Neath, however.

He also mentions 'Pont Rethewenne', which is a typical example of his inventive spelling. A possible interpretation is 'Pontrhydyfen'. For some reason his record of bridges in Glamorgan are very detailed, and they were confirmed later by Rice Meyrick. When one manages to decipher the spelling, he provides an invaluable picture of the considerable number of stone bridges in the County at this early time.

He found a 'Pont Newith of Stone' and a 'Wennybridge of Stone' in the Pen-y-bont ar Ogwr *(Bridgend)* area, and on the river 'Thawen' (the correct version is Afon Ddawen) he records the following: 'Pont Vain' *(Y Bont Faen)*; Pont Llanbleiddian, (for once he had the correct spelling, 'Pont Landough'; 'Pont Melinehe', 'Pont Kingman', and a 'Pont Newith'. He gives an accurate description of bridges on Afon Elái *(the Ely river)* which he describes as 'Notable Bridges on the Lay River'. They were: 'Pont Eniselthan' of wood; 'Pont Rethe Yevan' of wood; 'Pont Filin Fawr' of wood (Miskin); 'Pont Rethsaran' of wood; 'Pont Llampeter' of three arches (Peterstone); 'Pont St Ffagans', a stone bridge of three arches; 'Pont Lay', two arches of stone; and 'Pont Lecwith', three arches of stone. Of these, only the latter remains in anything like its original form. His report suggests that Glamorgan had a larger complement of stone bridges than most other parts of Wales at that time.

The next traveller to provide detailed information on the position of bridges was Edward Llwyd (1660?-1709) Llwyd's parents were country landowners, his father from Oswestry and his mother from the Prys family of Goginan in Ceredigion. Edward spent some of his early years at his local school near Oswestry, before going on to Winchester and from there to Oxford in 1682. He also spent some years as a schoolteacher, and probably had more than a passing knowledge of the Welsh language.

In 1693 he was asked to research a book on Celtic history, which during the next seven years was to take him through the British Isles as well as a short but disastrous visit to Brittany where he found the inhabitants less helpful than the Welsh because they promptly threw him into prison.

His tour of Wales, which took place between 1697 and 1699, involved visiting every parish where he distributed questionnaires in an attempt to gain as much information as possible about local history. His contribution was considered to be the most important part of the survey, and the part dealing with Wales was published a couple of years after he finished his travelling in 1701.

His knowledge of Welsh enabled him to record with a reasonable degree of accuracy the names of all the bridges in each parish he visited, however small or insignificant they were. His work is believed to have filled twenty-two chests, which included some one hundred and seventy handwritten volumes.

Living as he did in an age when six figure map references were unknown, even the few maps available were often inaccurate, and it is hardly surprising that it is hard to locate many of the bridges he named. His book *Archaeologica Britannica*, and the information that has survived has left us with an unique list of names of the earlier Welsh bridges. There are far too many to list here, but the following relates to the area between Machynlleth and Dolgellau.

'Pont Cymerau over the river Dulais about 20 yards or less above ye place where nant Ceiswyn falls into Dulais.' He notes 'Pont Abercorris on the same river. About a mile lower near Corris Brook' he records 'Pont Carnion and Pont Kisselgwn' (Cesailwen).

His map reference for the latter was: 'a mile from the church and an arrows flight from its outfall.'

As mentioned earlier the maps of the period were very inaccurate and it was some considerable time before bridges, or even river crossings generally, were marked. The first maps of any value are those of Ogilvy, who marked his routes through Wales in the form of road strips, and many of Llwyd's names and locations can be matched with his crossings.

By the early 18th century the number of travellers visiting Wales for pleasure, as opposed to those who came earlier on a specific mission, had increased considerably. Most of them published books describing various places they visited and their experiences during the journey. Some like Daniel Defoe, of Robinson Crusoe fame, was not particularly impressed with the mountains and the weather, and although others gave a fairer picture, they were English Gentry with little or no knowledge or true interest in rural Wales.

One of the few exceptions was Thomas Pennant 1726-98, who owned estates in Flintshire and his *Tours of Wales* reflect his widespread interest in such diverse subjects as herbs, rocks, and antiques, but gives very little information about the bridges of the period.

Inscriptions

Only a very few bridges built during the 18th and 19th century bear inscriptions, and coming across a plaque giving details of construction and possibly the name of the builder can be a fascinating discovery.

The most common inscription is a simple date, and possibly the initials of the person who built the bridge. The letters were usually carved on a sandstone plaque, which was normally built into the parapet. More often than not these would be on the inside, but the one on Pont Aberteifi *(Cardigan Bridge)* is on the outside, making it almost impossible to read unless you are an abseiling expert. There is little doubt that it was moved from a more prominent position during repairs, probably having being retained from an earlier bridge. It states:

This arch was built in ye year 1726, W. Jones.

This is one of the earliest dates recorded, surpassed only by the one on Pont Llechryd, a little higher up Afon Teifi which, although badly worn, is generally considered to read '1655'. This plaque was also removed from an earlier bridge and mounted on a later one, a common practice among bridge builders and repairers. The date 1743 can be seen on a bridge over Nant Clarach just west of Plas Gogerddan near Aberystwyth (at OS 629836).

In some cases the date is inscribed in Roman Numerals. A good example, once again badly worn and of an earlier date than the present bridge, can be seen on the inside of the upstream parapet of Pont Aberbrân near Welshpool, which states: 'Erected by James Parry in MDCCXCI. I will not spoil your fun by converting it into figures.

Plaques stating the name of the original builder, although his work will probably have been much repaired or even reconstructed, are both interesting and important historical pointers. Most of them are found on mid to late-19th century bridges and often include the surveyors name as well. From the beginning of the 20th century Cardigan County Council would place an inscribed plaque, bearing the name of the builder and County Surveyor, on most of its new bridges. Many of these plaques were bilingual, the first appearing on the top bridge at Pontarfynach *(Devil's Bridge)* in 1901. During the next few years the name of Roderick Lloyd, the County Surveyor, appeared regularly on the plaques. The one exception to this rule in Ceredigion took place when a bridge was eventually built over the ford at Nantystalwyn on the old drove-road from Abergwesyn to Tregaron in 1928. The County decided to honour its road foreman for his many years of loyal service. This plaque read:

Built in 1928 by the employees of Builth Wells and Tregaron R.D.C.S. Labour Foreman Tom Ebeneser.

For some reason there are more inscriptions on the bridges of Ceredigion than anywhere else in Wales, although Brycheiniog (*Breckonshire*) faithfully recorded any repairs during the 1930s. They also named the bridge, which can be of great interest as some, like 'Pont-y-Bat', have very unusual names. A plaque on the large stone bridge, just before reaching Pont Sarn Viaduct from Cefn Coed, states that GLAIS BRIDGE NO. 200 was widened in 1935. All County bridges are numbered on the survey records, but to my knowledge, this is the only plaque that displays the survey number with the name of the bridge.

Maldwyn (*Montgomeryshire*) also reminded their bridge users of the efforts of their surveyor Thomas Penson. He was well known for his work on iron bridges in the County, although his name does not appear on these. A difficult to read plaque on the outside of the downstream parapet of Llanidloes Short Bridge states:

Thos. Penson, County Surveyor, E.D. Jones Builder.

Bridge building was often a big job and it was common practice to employ a number of masons. There would hardly be room on a small plaque to record all their names, but the original builders of Pont Henllan over Afon Teifi managed to squeeze all their initials in: OZE, JD, JT, JE, JJ, 1744.

The builders of Pont y Pump *(The bridge of five)* near Llangrannog however were determined that their efforts should not go unrecorded. Not only were the names of J. Owen, T. Evans, J. Davies, G. Griffiths, D. Jones together with the date 1884 inscribed on two plaques, but the bridge was also named after them.

When a bridge was finally completed, often after years of struggling to raise funds, the contributors would often insist that future users of the crossing would never be allowed to forget their generosity. One such bridge is the fine large stone arch at Alltcafan near Llandysul. The sandstone plaque on the inside of the west parapet provides the complete story.

This bridge was built, the approaches formed and the road from Rhyd Fach to Llandussul made through the exertions of John Lloyd Davies esquire, of Blaenffynnon, who from conviction of its benifit to the county projected the work and proqured the money necessary to execute it in the years 1839-40-41.

44

One of the longest inscriptions can be seen on a large slate slab set into the upstream recess of Builth Wells bridge, giving details of its original builder and all those involved in its later rebuilding. A similar large slab commemorates the history of Haverfordwest Bridge (Pont Hwlffordd).

During the middle ages the church took on the responsibility of building and maintaining the main stone bridges of the time. The Arms of the Bishop of St Asaph, carved on a slate slab, was found on Llangollen bridge during rebuilding in the last century, and a sandstone plaque of the same arms could be seen until recently on the parapet of Rhuddlan bridge. The coat of arms of Thomas Johnes of Hafod were built into Pont-Blaen when it was erected in 1783. There is, surprisingly, not an inscription, and the two shields that bear the arms are on the outside of the parapets and difficult to view.

Apart from the Welsh half of the bilingual plaques on Cardiganshire Bridges, the use of the Welsh language is rare in bridge inscriptions. The only piece of poetry, that I am aware of, is a very poor example of an 'englyn', that can be found on Pont-rhyd-y-gwaed, on the main road from Rhuthun to Denbigh, at Rhewl.

The plaque on an insignificant bridge over Afon Cwerchyr at Aber-banc, Ceredigion (355419) issues a pearl of wisdom.

Ymdeithydd clyw yr hyn a ddywed y bont. Trwy Undeb y Cyfoethog ar Tlawd yr adaeladwyd fi. Undeb sydd nerth.

The inscription is on a sandstone shield. In English, it means:

Traveller listen what the bridge says. Through the unity of the rich and the poor I was built. Unity is strength.

From around the 1920s until fairly recently a bronze plaque became the normal way of adding an inscription to a bridge. The one on Cardiff (Canton) bridge, opened in 1931, lists all the dignitaries taking part in the ceremony. It is, however, pleasing to see that stone plaques with neatly cut letters never disappeared completely in Wales, and one such inscription commemorates one of the few visits of Cabinet Ministers to rural Wales in the 1930s. The new Pont Gwanas near Dolgellau was opened by Herbert Morrison, Minister of Transport in 1936, and the plaque duly records the fact.

Details of each individual inscription is given with the description of the bridge concerned. Inscriptions commemorating demolished bridges are rare, but a plaque set into the garden wall of a house in Y Bontfaen (*Cowbridge*), Glamorganshire, states:

45

A bridge of very ancient origin over the river and alongside this road was widened and improved in 1911.

The remainder of the inscription is barely legible, and is of no importance as it only lists the names of the councillors involved. It is probable that the bridge referred to was the one depicted by Gastineau in *Wales Illustrated*.

Construction Techniques

It is reasonable to assume that ancient man, faced with a river, would attempt to wade through at a shallow place. As he acquired building skills and tools, he would fell trees and lay them across from one bank to the other, supporting them in mid stream on pillars of stone whenever possible.

This *clapper* or *lintel* type bridge, which are far more common in the West Country than they are in Wales, are considered to be the oldest type of river crossings found in Britain. Being of prehistoric origin, those still surviving are probably no earlier than medieval.

The practice of laying long slabs of stone on crudely constructed piers was the obvious way to provide a fairly permanent crossing and although such techniques required considerable manpower, it would be relatively easy compared to the building of long barrows and cromlechs. We do not know for certain what type of bridges the Romans built during their occupation of Wales, or even if they built any at all. Some historians suggest that they crossed all major rivers by fording them, possibly with the use of large stepping stones, or wooden piles driven into the river bed. There is not a scrap of evidence that the large number of ancient looking stone bridges situated in the vicinity of a known Roman road, are of Roman origin.

This has not prevented people from attributing many old stone bridges to the Romans. The two best known are the old bridge at Penmachno, and Pont Sarn-ddu in the Lledr valley. So convinced are many that the latter, one of the few 'lintel' type bridges surviving in Wales, is of that early period that British Rail have named the nearby station 'Roman Bridge'. The truth is that there is no bridge in Wales that can be remotely considered to be of Roman origin, and any so described on early postcards can be ignored.

Some records exist of stone bridges being built during the 13th century, but the vast majority were of wood. Up until the beginning of the 18th century, stone bridges in Wales were the exception rather than the rule. The type of bridge normally found in the middle ages was of the 'A' frame construction, so often depicted in Western films. This type of construction was exceptionally strong and the ease with which they were often blown up on the silver screen is totally misleading.

During flood prevention work near the Monnow Bridge in Gwent the remains of large baulks of timber in the river bed confirmed that an earlier bridge had been of this type. The main strength of this type of construction was its ability to withstand pressure from above, but they were vulnerable to flood damage, particularly on wide rivers where large amounts of debris gathered in the frames, causing a build up of water pressure.

In order to prevent this regular disaster, stone piers were often constructed and timber beams or whole trees laid across the top. Smaller pieces were laid on these to fill the gaps, and the whole was then covered with earth and gravel. Cheap and easy to construct, this became the mainstay of bridge building well into the late Middle Ages. This type of bridge was still being used in the Lledr valley until quite recently, and the remains of many can still be seen there.

The great breakthrough in bridge building came with the perfection of arch construction, although it was some time before this became the common method of bridge construction.

Where solidity was not available for the foundations of the abutments and the piers, it was necessary to either excavate or drive wooden piles deep into the mud, until bedrock could be reached. Wych Tree Bridge at Morriston, built by William Edwards, rested on a large number of oak piles driven into the mud and through to the shale below. When the bridge was demolished, after almost 200 years use, they were still in perfect condition. Similar piles were found during the building of the new bridge at Leckwith, Cardiff in the mid-1930s.

The best examples of trestle type bridges in Wales are those built by the Cambrian Railway Company over the Mawddach and Dwyryd estuaries, although plans to build a similar crossing over the Dyfi failed when, even after pile driving, solid foundations could not be achieved.

Arch building was a highly skilled operation restricted to a few specialist builders. Having secured firm abutments, the 'former' for the arch would be secured over wooden scaffolding. The carpenters who fixed the formers played an important role in the construction of the bridges, but few received any credit for their work. The complex methods of laying the scaffolding has been recorded by some of the travellers and artists of the period. Those of particular note are Colt Hoare's illustrations of Chirk Aqueduct and Newport Bridge during construction.

The building of a large railway viaduct must have been spectacular to watch. The embankment would be brought up as far as possible to facilitate the transport of materials; two piers would be built to arch height, and the former fitted. While the arch was being built, another pier would be constructed ready for the carpenters to fit the next former, and so on over the entire length of the viaduct. Once the arch ring was built, temporary roadways in the form of planking would be laid on top, as the builders moved outwards, ever outwards.

Living, as we are, when steel scaffolding can be erected and dismantled in a short space of time, it is difficult to imagine that the erection of the timber supports, often in a fast flowing river, was a more difficult task than building the arch itself. Disasters could and often did occur during this operation.

The first layer of stones to be built over the former are known as 'arch rings' and in some cases, they are inserted as two layers, hence the term 'double arch rings'. The layers would often vary in size, and on some of the larger bridges decorative stonework would be used resulting in a most attractive arch. There was considerable scope for decoration when bricks were used, as can be seen on some of the arched railway bridges.

The arch would be held in position by the keystone, a wedge shaped stone inserted into the middle of the arch, often going through one or more layer and protruding outwards from the face. This type is known as a projecting keystone, and was sometimes used to bear some form of inscription, usually letters or a date.

The positioning of the arch rings and the keystone were of vital importance to the strength of the bridge. Pressure on top of the arch will force the key stone down, keeping the arch firmly in position. On the other hand, too much weight on the haunches can force the keystone upwards, causing the whole structure to collapse; a fate that befell William Edwards' second attempt at Pontypridd. In order to lighten the weight in the haunches (also known as spandrels), circular holes are built into the masonry. The longer the span the bigger the problem, and in order to keep the weight to a minimum on his massive one hundred and forty-four foot span at Pontypridd, the builder even resorted to filling the roadway with charcoal.

Bridges without parapets are uncommon. The low wall is, after all, what lays between a secure roadway and an early bath. Parapets tend to vary from bridge to bridge, from as low as two feet (60cm) to as high as four or five feet (1.5-1.8m). Often dislodged by heavy vehicles, pushed over by vandals, or simply taken as convenient building material, to come across a bridge without a parapet does not in itself imply that they did not originally exist.

Towards the end of the nineteenth century brick began to replace dressed stone as the main material for bridge building. Many of the railway bridges built at that time used brick, which had the advantages of being cheaper to buy and much easier to handle. It does not take much imagination to realise the difficulty in handling large heavy blocks of stone in all weathers, at upwards of a hundred feet (30 metres) on wooden scaffolding of doubtful stability. Brick of the ordinary red type had the disadvantage of not being particularly long lasting, which accounts for the poor condition of many brick bridges today. A far more durable variety of brick was the blue engineering type, mostly obtained from Staffordshire. All the main aqueducts on the Montgomery Canal were rebuilt with them, as well as the piers of some of the later South Wales Railway Viaducts.

The building of bridge piers in a river bed involved the creation of a coffer dam, a temporary construction to keep the water at bay while the foundations were dug out and the mortar allowed to dry. In deep fast flowing rivers that were difficult to divert, and in tidal waters, building a coffer dam was a major construction project in itself. During the building of Newport Town Bridge, Malkin states that David Edwards

> had to endure Welsh mountain floods from the land and furious Severn tides from the Bristol Channel, but he surmounted every obstacle and completed it in 1801.

An essential part of any pier is the cutwater. They were pointed on most bridges, and were built to cut the water like the prow of a ship. When built up to road level the triangular section at the top would form a recess where unwary pedestrians, caught halfway across with a coach and horses bearing down on them, could find refuge. Some examples can be seen where an enterprising builder built a seat into the recess, ideal for fishermen or those intent on sitting and staring at the water. When the bridge was wide enough not to require a recess, the cutwaters would terminate about halfway up, often in a stepped construction or some other form of decoration. Pont Llandrinio near Welshpool has an interesting ball finial above the cutwaters.

Arches are usually described by whatever part of a circle they represent (pointed arches being rare), for example segmental, or semicircular. Railway arches, because of their height and narrow openings, were often elliptical. Bearing in mind the almost insurmountable problems in some aspects of bridge building during the 18th and 19th century, it was not surprising that the work on a large crossing was spread over a number of years. Work would often only take place during the summer months, when the water level was low. William Edwards' three attempts at Pontypridd took ten years to complete, with many more projects taking four or five years each.

The first arches were of a small span, resulting in the need for several piers to cross a wide river. Very few of the pointed Norman arches survive, 'Pont Spwdwr' being the best example, although some pointed arches were built at a later date to match the original during rebuilding, as at Dolgellau, or as a special feature by a builder who wanted to be different or was doubtful of his ability to construct a segmental arch. Gradually as techniques improved arches became wider, but solid foundations were always a problem. Some of the bridges of North Wales, built over boulder strewn rivers, have arches of different sizes for no other reason than the need of suitable rocks for a foundation. Pont y Pair in Betws-y-coed is a fine example of a builder using available foundations, and ending up with two arches of different sizes.

Building a new bridge over a fast flowing or tidal river was often such a difficult enterprise that it was not unknown for the construction to take place on dry land some distance away, and the river to be later diverted under it.

An important insight into medieval bridge building methods was obtained when Bont Fawr, Pontarddulais was demolished in the late 1940s. It has long since been argued that it should have been saved, but as the two original pointed arches had been covered by later bridges, there was in reality very little left that was worth preserving. A number of medieval bridges had been removed prior to this one, with little or no public concern. But in this case the engineer undertaking the work had the foresight to carry out an accurate survey, and he produced detailed notes of its construction once the later masonry had been dismantled.

The mortar was analysed and found to be medieval, and the pointed arches were similar in design to nearby Pont Spwdwr, a listed bridge built in the early 16th century. The arches were built of thin stones and there was no indication that they had been 'dressed' in any way. On top of the arch, a layer of clean sieved soil had been laid, followed by a pavement of six inch (15cm) stones. The next layer consisted of what was described as 'land stones', some two inches (5cm) in size, on top of which was laid a six inch (15cm) deep layer of slightly larger pieces of limestone. The original arch was nine and a half feet (2.9m); the parapets eighteen inches (46cm) on each side. The widening that followed was a yard (0.9m) on one side, and seven feet (2.1m) on the other, and a further two arches had been rebuilt. At a later date a further widening took place at one corner.

The original arches were the second on the Cardiff side and the first on the Caerfyrddin side. Photographs taken during demolition, and the testimony of archaeologists who examined the structure, appear to confirm that these two arches were amongst the oldest that have so far been exposed in Wales.

Demolished Bridges

This book attempts to record most of the well known Welsh bridges that are, hopefully, still standing. It may appear rather pointless to dwell on those that have long since disappeared, but to quote a museum which sometime said 'history started yesterday', no survey of bridges can be complete without some reference to some of the well known landmarks that have been demolished in the last fifty years or so.

Old buildings, bridges, and other sites considerd to be only of borderline historic importance are being destroyed at an alarming rate, often because they stand in the way of development. But in many cases, the cost of maintaining them in reasonable conditon has become too great for a cash starved Local Authority, or a private individual deprived of suitable grants.

The choice is often between the cost of demolition and that of making a structure safe. The cost of dismantling a large bridge can sometimes be astronomical compared to the cost of a little regular maintenance.

When demolition is the only answer, the army often oblige as part of a training exercise. During the time I was researching the South Wales Valleys, I asked a colleague who was an engineer in the Territorial Army if he had 'blown any bridges lately'. He replied that he had, and went on to describe, sparing me none of the gory details, the destruction of a fine tramway bridge. A few days later a friend, who knew the area well and was assisting me with my research, mentioned with great enthusiasm that he had remembered the whereabouts of a fascinating bridge. It took only a few sentences to realise which bridge he was referring to, and I had to cut him short and point out that the army had beaten us to it.

Since the end of the Second World War, the closure of many of the South Wales Valleys small branch lines has resulted in a number of viaducts being rendered obsolete. A few of the larger stone masterpieces have survived through preservation orders, or simply because of the high cost of demolition. Most of the lattice girder and brick pier types had to go because they were often unsafe, or because there was not enough money available to preserve all of them.

Crymlyn Viaduct, 214986

One such bridge to be sacrificed was the world famous viaduct at Crymlyn in Monmouth. Built in 1862 by T.W. Kenard and designed by Charles Liddell it was, at the time, the third highest bridge of its type in the world. The original plan was to construct it as a stone viaduct, but there was concern that the high winds in the area would make it unstable. It was decided that a braced cast iron structure of tubes and girders resting on brick piers would reduce the bulk of cross section exposed to the winds. It was the longest rail bridge in the country, consisting of two spans of one thousand and sixty feet (323m) and five hundred and eighty four feet (178m), with a small hillock in between. Each span was one hundred and fifty feet (45m) in length, and at its highest point it was two hundred and eight feet (85m) above the river bed.

When it was closed in 1952 it was scheduled for preservation, but it received no maintenance, and had to be demolished in 1967. Its end was used as the finale for the film *Arabasque*, in which it was bombed, shelled, and had a train derailed over it. At least it survived long enough to be demolished by the nation who built it – during the war it was considered a prime target for enemy bombers, but it was never attacked. All that remains of this spectacular crossing are the two end abutments, numerous picture postcards and photographs, and plenty of memories.

At the time there was considerable hard feeling about the closure of many of the small branch lines, but there must have been many travellers who were secretly glad that they would never again have to endure a journey across Crymlyn Viaduct on a dark windy night.

Pwll-y-pant, 151893

The railway viaduct at Pwll-y-pant crossed the Rhymney Valley (*Cwm Rhymni*) near Llanbradach. Built by the Barry Railway in its attempt to poach the Eastern Valley coal trade, it was similar in construction to the Walnut Tree viaduct at Taff's Well, made of lattice girders resting on Blue Staffordshire bricks. It was built in 1901, and from the outset there was a legal confrontation with the coal owners, who claimed compensation on the grounds that they could no longer mine the land underneath. The legislation dragged on for years until in 1936 the railway company decided that the cost of compensation was greater than the value of the line, and the bridge was dismantled. At one hundred and twenty-five feet (38m) high and two thousand four hundred feet (731m) long, it was a spectacular crossing, and some idea of its size can still be seen as the western abutment and one arch still remain. As late as the early 1960s the masonry could still be seen, strewn across the valley where it fell.

Walnut Tree Viaduct, 125829

Built at the same time as Pwll-y-pant, and in the same materials, it was removed in 1970 to make way for the new A470 road. There are two arches remaining, hidden among the trees above the Gwaelod-y-garth road. The remaining pier was used as an unofficial display site by a local man to commemorate the Queens Jubilee in 1977, and the vivid yellow lettering is still visible. The viaduct was a little over one hundred feet (30m) high and one thousand five hundred and forty eight feet (472m) in length.

Quakers Yard Viaduct, 084867

Railway builders wishing to cross the Taf Valley (Dyffryn Taf) went for the narrowest point just north of Quakers Yard, and one viaduct is still in use. The other two, a little higher, suffered badly from mining subsidence, and during their latter years the arches had to be shored up with timber supports, which did little to inspire confidence among passengers despite a ten mile (16km) an hour speed limit. They survived until the line was closed to passengers in 1951, and they were finally demolished in 1960. The one remaining abutment can be seen from the A470, on the western side of the valley.

In the Rhondda Fach the best known viaduct was the long timber trestle crossing at Aberdâr. Brunell built it in the 1860s, and in fact wanted a stone viaduct. As was often the case in South Wales he was overruled by the Railway Companies, on the grounds of cost. It was similar to one he built in the West Country, and he had no faith in its construction. It was dismantled in 1946, having had a much longer life than the famous designer had professed. No traces remain, but the few photographs indicate that it was a handsome structure.

The industrial counties of south-east Wales have lost more stone road bridges than any other part of Wales, due to the industrialisation of the valleys where suitable land for road building was at a premium. One bridge to be sacrificed to progress was old Cardiff bridge. Built by James Parry of Hay during the latter years of the 18th century it was a superb example of a masonry bridge of the period. It had three large arches over the river, with two smaller ones on either side to cope with the floodwater. The illustrations by J.G. Wood shows it to have semicircular arches and a steep approach at each end. It was replaced by the present Canton bridge in 1931.

Of the nine bridges attributed to be the work of William Edwards, only two survive in anything like their original form, at Pontypridd and Llanymddyfri. His son, David Edwards, was also a bridge builder of note, although most of his work has also now disappeared. His most important bridge was the famous one at Newport. Completed in 1801 he had to 'surmount such problems as floods, the high Severn tides, and the difficulties of finding suitable foundations' as Malkin reported. The bridge was fifty seven feet (17.5m) from low water to the top of the parapet, and had five arches, the centre arch having a span of seventy feet (21m). It, together with the one at Cardiff, were probably the most attractive bridges to be demolished to make way for urban development. Malkin describes it as a 'very ornamental, magnificent and scientific bridge which cost 10, 165 pounds to build'. A number of postcards and other illustrations have survived, and there is a particularly fine print by Colt Hoare, that was sketched during its construction.

Malkin lists nine bridges that were built by William Edwards, but admitted he did not know all of them, and it is possible that this great builder and designer was responsible for the erection of as many as a dozen bridges, mostly in South Wales. Some had a very short life, but the only one to be destroyed by flood was at Glasbury.

His Beaufort Bridge over Afon Tawe was a handsome three arch crossing, and took its name from the local estate of that name. It was still in excellent condition when removed in 1968. Of the others built by him Pontycymer was replaced by a ferro-concrete bridge in the mid-1930s, and his fine effort at Pontardawe was largely rebuilt around the middle of the 19th century.

Wych Tree Bridge, 214986

The greatest loss of any of William Edwards' bridges was that of 'Wych Tree Bridge' at Morriston, so named because of a Wych Elm that grew nearby. He started work on the bridge in 1779, to a design closely based on the Pontypridd crossing. It had a single span of ninety-five feet (29m), with two round openings of eight feet (2.4m) and two feet (0.6m) in each abutment. Finding suitable foundation proved a problem, and he had to drive oak piles, through clayey sand and gravel, into blue clay.

The bridge carried heavy traffic for almost two hundred years. During the war 100 ton tanks passed over without damaging the structure. When a new bridge became necessary to cope with the heavy volume of modern traffic, attempts were made to preserve the bridge as an ancient monument. The adjoining land had to be purchased for a new bridge, and at the time a small steelworks occupied this site. They were unwilling to sell, and with much reluctance the bridge was dismantled in 1959. The steelworks closed a few years later, but it was too late by then to save this fine old bridge.

With the current public awareness in our industrial heritage, councils are finding it far more difficult to remove bridges without good cause. A few, however, still disappear when they could have been saved. Canal bridges, due to their awkward approaches and narrow widths are very susceptible to the road planners wrath. Even as late as 1973 Pont-ar-Darrel in Brecon was removed although it had earlier been listed in a *Publication on Ancient Buildings of Wales, (Powys)*.

Only a few of the small cast iron bridges built to span streams and canals in South Wales survived the clearing of industrial wastelands. A small footbridge is still in use at the top end of the car park in Maesteg, and one dismantled at Rhyd-y-car in Merthyr has been partly re-erected opposite Chapel Row, the birthplace of Joseph Parry the composer.

One of the best examples of such bridges spanned Afon Taf at the bottom of Castle Street in Merthyr, and was dismantled in 1963. Such was the concern of local residents, who considerd it to be second only in importance to the one at Ironbridge, that the local authorities 'preserved' the remains by dumping them in a corner of nearby Cyfarthfa Park.

The bridge was designed by Wadkin George, the Cyfarthfa works engineer, and its construction was something of an urgency as the previous stone bridge had finally succumed to Afon Taf flooding the previous year. Work started on erecting the bridge in the summer of 1799, and it was completed a year later. It was to become a vital link between Ynysfach, Grangetown, and the town itself. The bridge was sixty-eight feet (21m) in length, and built in three separate sections. The road surface of cobbled stone was set into the framework. It was thirteen feet (4m) wide and formed a gentle curve, with handrails serving as parapets. It was in constant use, but by 1852 concern was being felt about its condition. The local Board of Health were told that it was 'unsafe for traffic in its present state'. Suggestions for a new bridge were ignored, and it is presumed that some repairs were carried out.

In 1860 its importance was highlighted when a census, carried out during a week in June, showed that a total of 57,716 foot passengers, 773 horses, 1881 wheeled vehicles, and 507 cattle crossed over it.

Eventually a new bridge was built, but the old structure still served as a pedestrian crossing. Jervoise considered it to be of sufficient importance to illustrate it in his book on Ancient Bridges, one of the few iron bridges granted that honour. Its sudden demolition in 1963 was viewed with horror by many local people.

In 1988, the bridge featured in an article in the press when the local authorities announced that they had called in a consultant to examine the remains, and report on the possibility of re-erecting it on a suitable site. It was discovered that many of the original pieces had been lost, destroyed or possibly stolen during the twenty five years that it had laid, rusting, in the park. The estimate of fifty-five pounds for its re-erection would now prove to be far too low, and its chances of ever spanning Afon Taf, or any other river, are now very remote.

Prior to its demolition, there had been speculation that its remarkable resistance to rusting was due to some secret formula, but chemical analysis proved this was not the case, and the present condition of the remaining castings prove this point.

It is possible that the bridge featured as an engraving, dated 1811, in Woods *Principal Rivers of Wales Illustrated*.

One of the largest stone arch railway viaducts to be demolished in recent years was the huge Barry Railway crossing over Dyffryn Elái *(Ely valley)* west of Cardiff. It came down in a spectacular explosion, at the second attempt (1983), on a damp Sunday morning to make way for an M4 link road using part of the track. The last stone river bridge with medieval origins to be demolished in South Wales was over Afon Llwchwr *(Loughor River)* at Pontarddulais. It had been bypassed before the war, and was removed in 1945. There were four arches, two of which were pointed and still remaining at the time of its destruction. Its original width was only eight feet (2.4m), but it had been widened on both sides, around the middle of the 19th century.

Pont Caerfyrddin *(Carmarthen Bridge)*

During the first half of the 20th century a number of stone bridges were demolished as part of road improvement schemes, often with little consideration given to their possible preservation. A few, however, were removed with reluctance after the local authorities decided that they could not be bypassed, and could not be improved sufficiently to meet the needs of modern traffic. One bridge to meet such a fate was the one of seven arches, crossing Afon Tywi at Caerfyrddin. Originally there were only six arches but a further one, of a different shape, was built in 1775. There have been suggestions, unconfirmed by any documentary evidence, that the original was built on dry land and the river diverted to run underneath it, probably in order to bring the port closer to the town.

A bridge existed here in the 13th century, and it is recorded that it was 'broken' in 1223 and again in 1233, when it was rebuilt with the aid of the Earl of Pembroke.

In 1326 a licence was granted to the 'good men of Kermerden' to charge a toll on boats using the river and apply the money towards the repair of the bridge. The bridge was repaired many times during the 15th century, and was widened by six feet (1.8m) when the extra arch was built in 1775. It was widened again in 1828. It suffered a great deal of flood damage; in 1831 it was in danger of being washed away and was only saved by removing part of the wall. A further catastrophy was averted in 1877 when, during another severe flood, forty baulks of timber chained together jammed against it, raising the water level to a dangerous height, but once again the bridge survived. It suffered more damage in 1931, and by this time it was considered to be the cause of flooding in the area and suggestions were put forward that it should be replaced.

When Jervoise inspected it at around this time he recorded it as being seventy-six yards (69.5m) long and seventeen feet wide (5.2m), having been widened on both sides resulting in the original stonework being hidden·in the core of the bridge.

In 1937 it was reluctantly decided that the bridge had to be demolished, and the present crossing was opened in April 1938.

A fine bronze plaque, badly in need of cleaning, depicting the old bridge has been set into the upstream parapet with a bilingual inscription on either side. The English version reads:

Carmarthen bridge 1936-38, built to replace a seven arch structure that became unsafe after several centuries of service.

Long Bridge, Risca

One of the best known tramways in South Wales was the one that ran down the Sirhywi valley in Gwent which resulted in the building of a remarkable masonry viaduct, abtly named Long Bridge at Risca. Consisting of a massive thirty-three arches, by far the largest number built in Wales, it delayed the completion of the line for some years, but was finally completed in 1810. Smaller viaducts consisting of a few arches had been built earlier, but Long Bridge was the first of the lengthy structures, and although only about 50 feet (15m) high was a very impressive feature as early illustrations show.

During the early years of the 20th century a section was blown down during a gale, the only bridge as far as I am aware, to have suffered such damage. It was never repaired and some years later the entire structure was demolished and the stone used to build a row of housed, suitably named Bridge Row.

A fine 19th century print confirms that the tramway followed a sharp bend around both ends which made it unsuitable for normal rail transport. It was bypassed in 1853 and was finally out of use by 1855.

Pont Sarn Offeiriad

This ancient clapper bridge of great, antiquity was situated over Afon Ystumiau in a remote mountain area above Dolwyddelan. It was so named from the tradition that priests used to ford the river there on their journeys to Ffestiniog. The only illustration appears to be a 'Valentine' post card from the 1920s. The area around it is heavily forested, and the blame for its destruction in the 1970s must surely be laid with the forestry road builders.

People remember demolished bridges with some affection, and did so over two hundred years ago when Edward Bevan penned this verse in memory of an old timber bridge at Newport, in 1760.

The old bridge I do remember,
Was built of famous oaken timber,
All but one pier in the centre,
That was built of stone and mortar.

Railway Bridges and Viaducts

Railway Viaducts more than make up in spectacular appearance for what they lack in age. The massive structure at Maes y Cymer near Hengoed was up by the mid-1850s, and others were to follow at regular intervals until the turn of the century. With the exception of a few in Clwyd, and the remote crossing over Cwm Prysor on the now defunct Bala-Trawsfynydd line, most of the large viaducts are confined to South Wales where the competition for rail networks was intense.

The area played a vital part in railroad development after a Trevethicks engine, the first of its kind in the world, puffed its way from Penydarren (Merthyr) to Navigation (Abercynon) in 1804. Some of the original track can still be seen, but the rapid developments of the next few years obliterated much of the historical line.

The need for a rail link between the iron town of Merthyr and the port at Cardiff became paramount to the exploitation of the mineral reserves because the only other means of transport, the Glamorgan canal, was already overcrowded and too slow.

Further west, small tramways had forged their way to the sea at Porthcawl and Britton Ferry, and later rail links were to use the same tracks. The Dyffryn Taf *(Taff Vale)* railway was in operation by the 1840s, and the following years saw severe competition between landowners for suitable rail links with the Bristol Channel ports. Most of the land was parcelled between the local landowners, who either had an active interest in the coal mines or levied a hefty toll on every loaded wagon that passed over their land. Every application for a new rail link had to be approved by Parliament and with most of the land owners also sitting as MPs, every bit of space was bitterly contested and everything possible was done to prevent a rival company from building a railway.

It is not surprising that many of the later rail companies had to resort to more difficult routes, once the easier access down the valleys had been taken by their competitors, or were for political or economical reasons beyond their reach.

One of the last companies into the field, the Barry Railway Co. often known as the spoilt child of the railways, protested, bullied, and forced its way through legal actions into the rail world, and even then found that it had to build two massive viaducts and several bridges in the space of twelve miles in order to reach the new port of Barry.

Railways heading south down the valleys had no great construction problems, once they had acquired the necessary land. Companies like the Llyfni Railway, the Port Talbot Railway (P.T.R.) and the Rhondda and

Swansea Bay (R. & S.B.) followed old tram lines, but later expansions caused the building of many bridges and viaducts, especially when the routes began to veer east to west across the valleys.

There were some splendid tunnelling achievements, notably the tunnel through to the Rhondda valley from Cwm Afan, but it was the spectacular viaducts that are our main interests here.

There were two basic methods of construction; the earliest types being stone built arches, often of heights around the one hundred feet (30m) mark. Towards the end of the 19th century, brick became the main material because it was cheaper to obtain and easier to handle, but lacked the long life expectancy of stone. The rail builders of the time had no idea that their wonderful examples of Victorian construction would be outmoded and abandoned in less than one hundred years.

The alternative to brick or stone arches were a series of lattice girders resting on piers of blue engineers bricks. Because they were easier to dismantle, and because the metal could be melted and reused, most of these viaducts have disappeared. One of the few to remain is Pontyberw near Pontypridd.

There is also the rail bridge category of 'over and under bridges', so called because of the position of the line. Once again, stone and brick were the main materials and there are some fine examples still to be seen, although if a line closed they were the first to suffer during road widening schemes due to their narrow openings. One such bridge to suffer this fate was one of three at Maesteg, built side by side within yards of each other, and of a particularly attractive elliptical arch.

A type of bridge much favoured by the Cambrian Railway in Mid Wales was the underpinned girder type. Here, the abutments were built of stone girders strung across, and sleepers bolted to them. They are the least attractive of any type of bridge, and although many are still in use, they are not likely to arouse much enthusiasm among readers of this book.

Large metal viaducts over wide river estuaries, coupled with the wood trestle type, are well known. The metal section usually opened to allow navigation to shipping, a legal requirement, and many are still in use as rail crossings. The reduction of shipping up most of our estuaries has rendered the metal section obsolete. Those at Llandore (Swansea) and at Neath are still in use, as are a few others that are a little smaller but just as interesting, and can be seen from the M4 motorway to the north of Swansea.

In North Wales, Pont y Bermo *(the Barmouth Viaduct)* is well known, and has recently undergone costly repairs. The trestle bridge over Afon

Dwyryd, on the same stretch of line, has a roadway on one side.

The mid-Wales line, forever being threatened with closure, has probably the two most attractive viaducts in Powys and Dyfed. The Cynghordy and Knucklas crossings are well worth the long journey just to see them.

In north-east Wales, the Chirk viaduct can be seen from the main road, but for those who make the effort to walk up to it, and break all the regulations by venturing on the track, it provides a grand view of barges on the aqueduct alongside. A large number of the surviving disused viaducts are now protected by preservation orders, but legislation arrived too late to save many others that were described in the chapter on Demolished Bridges. Many disappeared under protest and some defied the demolition gang at the last moment. St Brides viaduct over Dyffryn Elái *(Ely Valley)*, removed to make way for a link road, was only blown up at the second attempt.

Railway bridges are often less accessible than others, but all the main viaducts can be reached without difficulty. Often a view point some distance away is best, and these are mentioned in individual descriptions. Railway bridges are modern compared to road bridges – most were built during a sixty year period from around 1840 to the turn of the century, but are well worthy of close examination. Much of the material was obtained from tunnelling in the area, for example, the waste from the Talerddig cutting on the Cambrian line provided the stone for the bridges on that stretch of line.

A number of low stone arches were built to carry railway lines over streets and industrial sites in urban areas, and the usual practice was to brick up one side, either during construction or at a later date, and use them as workshops and storerooms. They also became the abode of vagrants, as portrayed in the well known music hall song, *Underneath the Arches*.

Such arches can still be seen, particularly in large cities such as Cardiff and Swansea. They lack the spectacular appearance of the high viaducts of the rural areas, but were built to the same exacting specifications.

All the best known railway viaducts are now Grade 2 listed structures.

Pont y Bermo *(Barmouth Railway Bridge)*, 625150 (124)

The building of a rail crossing over the Mawddach Estuary was the Cambrian Railway's greatest bridging achievement, and more than compensated for their failure to construct a similar bridge at Aberdyfi, because of foundation problems.

This impressive piece of railway engineering, on which my great grandfather was employed as a carpenter, is eight hundred yards (731.5m) long, making it the longest estuary crossing in Wales. The railway was built in stages along this often difficult stretch of coastline, and the bridge was completed in 1867 a short time before the link up at Dyfi Junction was completed. The first engine to use the line had to be towed across the Dyfi Estuary behind the ship *James Corley*, on a barge. It was based at Aberdyfi Quay and used to carry materials for the line construction as it moved north.

Pont y Bermo, for most of its length, is a wooden trestle construction on piles driven through the sand into solid foundations in the estuary bed. It is not easy to count the number of spans, of which there are supposed to be one hundred and thirteen.

In order to comply with Admiralty regulations at the time, a suitable type of opening had to be incorporated to allow free passage of sailing vessels. The deep water channel on the north side was bridged with what was known as a 'Cock and Draw' construction, and this iron section of the bridge has been the main cause of expense, which has created considerable speculation as to its life span.

A local gentleman, who was convinced that the bridge could not be built, promised to eat his hat on its completion. In October 1867 when the first proper train service had replaced the horse drawn carriages that had been in use since June of that year, he was taken to a restaurant in Barmouth and asked if he wanted it boiled or roasted. Before the crossing at Glandyfi (or Morben Junction to give it its first name) was completed, passengers from the north were ferried across to Ynys-las to connect with the Shrewsbury to Aberystwyth train. This shunting service took only thirty-three minutes, considerably quicker than the rail service replacing it along the northern side of Afon Dyfi. The problems foreseen with the opening section of the bridge were well founded, and the 'Cock and Draw' arrangement was replaced with a revolving opening in 1900, supplied by the Cleveland Bridge and Engineering Co. The wooden trestle section was rebuilt between 1906 and 1909 by Abraham Williams of Aberdyfi, and toll charges were introduced for pedestrians at both ends after completion of the work. Some years ago it was discovered that the trestles were badly affected by salt water termites, and there were fears that the bridge would be closed, but public pressure was such that British Rail finally agreed to the costly repairs necessary to keep the line open.

Dolgoch Viaduct, 651045 (135)

A small but impressive three arch viaduct, fifty-two feet (16m) in height, built to carry the Talyllyn Railway over the river at the beauty spot of Dolgoch Falls. Built in 1866, the line was closed in 1950 but partly reopened a year later. It is now fully operational as a tourist attraction. The viaduct, which is the main bridge construction on the line, was rebuilt during restoration work on the line in 1970.

Dyfi Valley Railway Bridges

Pont Glantwymyn, 843037 (135)

The Cambrian Railway Company's decision to drive a cutting through the Talerddig gap, rather than embark on costly tunnelling, was partly due to the shortage of building stone for the embankments and bridges as far as Machynlleth. A number of these were necessary to bring the line down as far as Glantwymyn, which was promptly named 'Cemaes Road', in common with railway builders policy at the time. Most of them are well worthy of closer inspection.

Afon Twymyn proved to be a serious obstacle, having to be bridged three times in a couple of miles, the most ambitious construction being the one at Glantwymyn itself. Although it falls far short of the large viaducts to be found in South Wales, it is an impressive crossing seventy feet (21m) above the river bed, consisting of a large centre arch with two smaller ones on either side. It was designed by G. Piercy and George Owen, and built as the line forged its way into the Dyfi valley in the early 1860s.

Viewing from the road does not do it justice, especially since there is a public footpath that leads to it from the modern flyover a little further down.

Pont Morben, 659979 (135)

Travellers who have had to endure the bleak windswept conditions often prevailing around Glandyfi Junction, as they changed trains for Pwllheli, will be only too aware of this bridge. But few will be familiar with its correct name of Pont Morben. The trestle structure that carries the line over Afon Dyfi was the best that the builders could manage across the estuary. They failed to build a similar crossing to the one at Y Bermo between Aberdyfi and Ynys-las, due to the unstable situation of the river bed. The bridge was not completed until 1867, being the last link to join the Cambrian Coast section with the Shrewsbury to Aberystwyth line. It has a span of one hundred and forty yards (128m), carried on seventeen timber and three iron spars. Regulations in force at the time compelled the buildings to include a thirty-seven foot (11m) opening for vessels, but with ship building on the upper reaches of the Dyfi curtailed when the line threw an embankment across the harbour at Derwen-las, the opening section was seldom used. It was finally converted to a fixed structure during repairs in 1914.

Glamorganshire Tram and Railway Bridges

Pont-rhyd-y-fen, 796942 (170)

All the large viaducts in Wales were built to carry a railway or a canal, but this one situated a short distance above the railway crossing, and towering above the village of Pont-rhyd-y-fen is quite unique. Originally built as an aqueduct, it later served as a tramway crossing, was filled in and used as a road, and is now a listed bridge carrying only a footpath.

The builder was John Reynolds, in 1823, who used it to carry water to supply his furnaces on 'Moel y Fen', where the water was also used to power a large wheel. It is, in all probability, the oldest stone viaduct in Wales, and the first major aqueduct to be built in the country.

Its four wide arches span Afon Afan, and the stonework has been repointed and restored in recent years, giving it a neat well kept appearance. There are bollards at both ends to stop cars. The bridge does now have parapets, and it offers a pleasant walk from one side of the village to the other without having to use the steep road. The structure is known locally as 'Y Bont Fawr' *(Big Bridge)* and is seventy-five feet (23m) high and four hundred and fifty nine feet (140m) in length with an overall width of around twelve feet (3.6m). Like most other viaducts of this type, it is a Grade 2 scheduled monument, and will hopefully be preserved for posterity.

Yard Bridge (Aber-crâ f) *(Abercrave)*, 815124 (160)

A large stone tramway bridge consisting of one massive arch with two openings in the spandrels. It was built in 1824 by Daniel Harper, with the intention of connecting up with the traffic on the Swansea Canal on the south-eastern side of Afon Tawe. Although a scheduled structure, it is covered in vegetation and is in need of maintenance, but is well worth viewing.

Aberdulais Railway Viaduct, 772995 (170)

This handsome stone structure with blue brick arches was built in 1850, before the line was actually opened, to replace Brunel's original timber bridge of 1846. There are five arches in all, one of which carries the road from Tonna to Aberdulais over a narrow iron bridge alongside. The abutments are those of the original bridge, and the difference between them and the remainder of the viaduct are obvious under close examination. It was still in use at the time of writing.

Gwauncaegurwen Viaducts, 700120 (160)

These two large viaducts were built of brick during the first decade of the 20th century, as part of the G.W.R. expansion to improve access from the coalfields of the area to Swansea Docks. The First World War put paid to the idea, and although the most northerly viaduct served a washery until recently, the other was never completed.

Llwydcoed Tramway Bridge, 990044 (170)

Although listed, this bridge is of no great significance, being typical of a number of other tramway crossings in the South Wales valleys. It was built by Evan Hopkin around 1803.

Pont Ty'n-y-garn *(Bridge)*, 895827 (170)

The bridge was built in 1829 to carry a tramway from Maesteg Iron Works to Porthcawl. It has three semicircular arches, and stepped cutwaters of an attractive design.

It now serves to carry a minor road, and is overshadowed by the motorway flyover. Some well meaning person has picked out the lettering on the plaque on the upstream parapet in black paint, which now clearly states,

> This bridge was erected in the year 1829 by Morgan Thomas, Laleston, Mason.

The stepped cutwaters are the most attractive feature on the bridge, and are typical of the work of the builder, which are also seen on Merthyr Mawr Bridge. The bridge is twelve feet (3.6m) wide, a handsome width for a tramway crossing of that period, and is still in excellent condition.

It is also known by the unusual name of Swannee Bridge, but I have been unable to discover any valid reason for this connection with an American river.

906894 (170)

Tramway bridge over Afon Garw, just south of Pont-yr-hyl. Built on a slope, it has two stone arches with brick arch rings. The date of construction is unknown, but is probably late 1820s. It is no longer in use, and was not adapted into a railway bridge as were many other tramway crossings.

684992 (159)

An interesting lattice girder bridge over Afon Tawe, built for the Swansea to Llanelli Central Wales link line at about the same time as Waungron Viaduct.

770903 (170)

A disused railway bridge over Afon Afan alongside the motorway flyover in Port Talbot. The original western side, some fifteen feet (4.6m) wide, is now in a state of deterioration. It was built to carry a tramway around the early 1840s. The eastern side was added in the 1880s when the Rhondda and Swansea Bay railway took over the track. The extra ten feet (3m) is quite visible under the northern arch, which serves a minor road. The other three arches span the river, and the bridge is built on a slight slope which results in the road arch being only a little over seven feet (2.1m) high. An ugly concrete wall separates the roadway from the river. The bridge is interesting in that it is a typical example of a tramway crossing that was later widened to carry a standard gauge railway.

Gwent Railway Viaducts

Blaenycwm, 133109 (161)

The third viaduct of the Heads of the Valleys Road can be seen opposite the Tredegar roundabout. The Abergavenny to Merthyr railway passed over the upper reaches of Afon Sirhywi here, one of the most exposed sections of line in South Wales, where during severe winters the line was blocked for days and sometimes weeks on end.

The viaduct, built by James Gardner in 1864 from local limestone with brick arches, has nine arches. The western side is now occupied by a housing estate but a good view can still be obtained from the road. It is in reasonable condition although beginning to show its age, and as there is no incentive to preserve the structure, will no doubt continue to decay.

Pontlotyn Viaduct, 115063 (161)

The interesting features of this bridge makes up for its lack of height, being only about twenty-five feet (7.6m) high. It was built in the 1850s over a couple of minor roads rather than a river and is an all stone construction of ten arches. It is still in use, which accounts for the pinning work carried out on a number of the arches. It is three hundred and sixty feet (110m) in length.

The Railway Inn has been built in three separate sections under the three eastern arches, which were presumably connected together by doorways cut through the arches. This fascinating building is somewhat ruined by the ugly, but no doubt necessary, public toilet in front. As I have never been inside during a time when a train passed overhead, I cannot comment on the result.

Bargoed Viaduct, 150003 (171)

The railway hugs the left bank of the Rhymni Valley and, when it has to cross Nant Bargoed, it does so in great style on a superb viaduct of dressed stone. There are ten arches built on attractive tapered piers, and the buttresses which supported the scaffold has been retained as a feature. The structure curves gently and drain pipes protrude from exactly the same position under each arch.

Some of the arches have been pinned, but if you can ignore this essential but disfiguring feature, it is a fine structure well worthy of admiration. It is seventy feet (21m) high and was built in 1856.

Usk Road and Railway Bridge, 375013 (171)

The present rail section, now disused, replaced a bowed girder bridge and is an ugly steel section supported on piers and hardly worth a second glance. The road section is partly a stone arch, to which has been added a similar steel section to provide the width needed for a second track.

The Coleford to Pontypool line which used the crossings was built in 1857 and closed in 1965.

Heads of the Valleys Viaducts

Tal-y-waun, 263043 (171)

This superb viaduct was built by the L.N.W.R. over a steep valley at Abersychan to carry the Blaenafon to Crymlyn section of the line. Built of dressed Pennant sandstone, with the middle of the nine arches towering well over one hundred feet (30m) above the river, it can be reached by turning off the B4246 and descending along the twisting narrow streets that lead to the valley floor.

The road arch on the western side is a separate structure, but on the eastern end a roadway passes under one of the big arches. On the bottom can be seen a plaque with the words, *Erected by John Gardner 1876-77*

M. Inst.GE. Engineer.

The arch rings are in blue bricks and there are pilasters at intervals below the parapets. The line was closed in 1954, but the viaduct remains in excellent condition. The best viewing point is from the northern side, where there has been less private development. On a sunny day, a walk underneath to the other side will show the fine weathered texture of the stonework. Although not as long, it is more impressive than Maesycwmer, and the builder has followed a gentle curve along the same line as at Cefn Coed and Clydach. It is a viaduct that is well worth a detour to see.

Clydach Viaduct, 233127 (161)

This crossing over a tributary of Afon Clydach is a handsome structure, and can be visited as part of a walk around the gorge that is famous for its remains of early iron works. Built in the early 1860s for the Abergavenny to Merthyr rail link, it has a gentle curve, similar to Cefn Coed but in this case determined by the contour of the hill.

The contractor was again John Gardner. He chose red sandstone rather than limestone as a building material, which has resulted in the viaduct having an attractive weathered appearance. Although it was a common enough practice to widen tramway bridges to take the standard line gauge, this appears to be the only big viaduct to have received such an addition. The original width was only thirteen feet (4m) and carried a single track. It was widened to carry a second line in 1877, taking the width up to twenty-six feet (8m). The widening took place on the upstream side, and this time the arches were built in blue bricks, one of the earliest example of their use in railway arches. The difference can be clearly seen from underneath.

71

Maes-y-cwmer Viaduct, 155949 (17)

This is another fine stone viaduct, which carried the Newport, Abergavenny and Hereford line over the Rhymni valley. Built by Charles Liddel in 1857, it has fifteen arches, and at seven hundred and seventy yards (704m) long and one hundred and twenty feet (36.5m) high, it is one of the oldest, longest, and highest railway viaducts surviving in South Wales. The construction was entirely of stone, and the arch rings are particularly impressive being made of large dressed blocks. The eastern arch, which spans the road, has been constructed at an attractive skew. The viaduct is very impressive when travelling down the valley, both A and B class roads passing underneath it, but the view back up the valley is obstructed by trees. The curve is best viewed from the public houses on the eastern side. There are barriers preventing access onto the viaduct.

Cefncoed Viaduct, 031077 (160)

The Victorian railway engineers, struggling to build railways across these valleys through almost impossible terrain, only achieved their task by building some of the longest and most spectacular viaducts in South Wales. The one at Cefncoed, north of Merthyr, is the third longest and carried the Brecon to Merthyr railway over Afon Taf Fawr.

The designer was Alexander Southerland, a friend of Richard Crawshaw the ironmaster, who exerted considerable influence over the construction work. The graceful curve was planned by him in order not to infringe on the land of another iron master. Crawshaw objected to the original plans to cross lower down, as he did not wish to have the viaduct within sight of his home at Cyfarthfa castle, but he was only partially successful as the crossing can still be seen from the front of the house.

The builders were Savin and Ward, and the opening day in August 1886 was a grand affair. There was room for celebration as the building had been beset with labour problems. In all, three hundred and fifty masons were employed on this contract and the one at Pontsarn, but the employment of a further fifteen non-union men brought about a strike. The original plan to build all of the viaduct using stone was abandoned, and when the masons were eventually forced back to work through poverty, bricks had been used to line the arches.

The viaduct has a maximum height of one hundred and fifteen feet (35m) and an overall length of seven hundred and twenty-seven feet (222m). Access on to the viaduct is no longer possible.

Like most of the other major railway viaducts, it is a Grade 2 listed structure and its future is secure. A good viewing place is from the A470

Merthyr bypass road, a short distance above.

Pontsarn Viaduct, 046099 (160)

Although smaller than Cefncoed this viaduct is just as impressive, spanning the wooded valley of Afon Taf Fechan, where there are no buildings to ruin its appearance. The designer and builders were the same as at Cefncoed, and both crossings were completed in 1886. It has seven arches, ninety feet (27.5m) high and is four hundred and fifty-five feet (139m) long.

There is a picnic site and parking place below the viaduct, and while in this area you may care to look at the small bridge that carries the minor road over the deep cataract. This road was an earlier Roman route over the Beacons. The present bridge, although it appears to be of a fair old age, was built as late as the middle of the 19th century to replace a wooden, and often very unsafe, crossing.

It is interesting to note that the arches of Pontsarn viaduct are built of stone as originally planned, which suggests that they had already been constructed before the strike that paralysed the work during the winter of 1885.

114767 (171)

A railway bridge of three arches, built by the Barry Railway Company during the last decade of the 19th century to link up with the G.W.R. line at St Fagans. The most notable features are the massive dressed stone cutwaters that have resisted the regular flooding of Afon Elai without a blemish, and the four courses of blue bricks that form the arch rings.

A couple of hundred yards further west, alongside the M4 link road, the construction of which demolished the fine viaduct over the valley, is another of the Barry Railway Company's fine bridges. The arch rings are again in blue bricks, as is the gently curving parapet.

The line was closed in 1930, and the bridge has been disused for more years than it spent as a working structure.

857961 (170)

A single span lattice girder bridge over Afon Afan at y Cymer. It was built in 1878 to connect the Llyfni Valley and Ogmore Railway to the South Wales Mineral Line.

The girders were ten feet (3m) apart and carried on wooden decking. The height above the river bed was one hundred and seven feet (32.6m). The original plan was to build a masonry viaduct of nine arches of forty feet (12.2m) each, but the contract did not materialise due to the lack of skilled labour.

The bridge was found to be unsafe, which hastened the closure of the line in 1970. The bridge still stands, but in order to deter motor cycle maniacs from using it, the abutments have been bricked up and the approaches bulldozed.

Pont-rhyd-y-fen Viaduct, 795942 (170)

One of the best known and most spectacular viaducts in southern Glamorgan, it was built of red brick in 1897 to carry the Rhondda and Swansea Bay Railway over the river and the houses. The area is still known as Tan-y-bont, *(Under the Bridge)*. Although only seventy feet (21m) high, it gives the impression of being much higher when viewed from below, which is in fact the best position. There are ten arches of a forty foot (12m) span. Although red brick was soon to be abandoned in favour of blue engineering bricks, the viaduct is still in superb condition, and a superb example of railway engineering of the period.

934986 (170)

A low lattice girder bridge over Afon Rhondda Fawr that carried the Rhondda and Swansea Bay Line to its junction with the Taff Vale Railway. Opened in 1890, it was closed in 1968.

857918 (170)

The only remaining bridge of three, within a few yards of each other at Maesteg, that carried the Port Talbot Railway over the road, river and the Llyfni Valley line. It was first used as a tramway bridge, and widened with bricks on the northern side to carry the railway. It has one of the finest elliptical arches in Glamorgan.

909889 (170)

One of several fine 'brick built' overbridges on the P.T.R. line, this one is just south of Pont yr-hyl. It has attractive decorative brickwork in the arch rings. It is still in good condition apart from damaged parapets.

Porthceri Viaduct, 604672 (171), Y Barri

This impressive structure is the only surviving viaduct built for the Barry Railway Company. It straddles the Porthceri Country Park, where it can be viewed from all sides. Undergrowth along the sides restricts the view of the end arches, but the whole sweep is best seen from the north-western side.

The viaduct was built by Pethwich Bros and Co. of Plymouth, and was modelled on a similar construction at Tavistock. Work began in August 1894 and ran into difficulties in its early stages. By 1896 the construction was suffering from subsidence, which was not disclosed to the Board of Trade inspectors. The builders would have been aware of the problems when they failed to reach solid bedrock during the building of the tenth and eleventh piers. These slipped before they were completed setting work back for months in 1896, during which time further excavations were necessary to reach a solid footing. But corners continued to be cut, with the result that the thirteenth pillar collapsed just before the viaduct was to be opened. The company was forced to build a loop line to bypass the viaduct while the repairing and rebuilding programme took place. The viaduct was not opened until 1900. It is still regularly used by trains carrying coal to the Aberthaw Power Station, and one can only marvel at the strength of the viaduct as a fully laden train passes over it.

At its highest point, the viaduct reaches one hundred and ten feet (33.5m) in height. There are thirteen arches, three of forty-five feet (13.7m) in width, and the remainder of fifty feet (15.2m), and it is an interesting challenge to pick out the different sizes. One fact, that is invisible to the naked eye, is that the northern end dips slightly. This is the result of subsidence that occurred during the early years of the bridge, but has long since stabilised enough to bear the heavily laden coal trains.

Pont-rhyd-y-cyff, 875894 (170)

Also known as the Cwm-du viaduct, it was built during 1897 to carry the Port Talbot Railway over the Darran valley at Llangynwyd. Built of red brick it reflects the changing use of materials during the latter years of the 19th century. Brick was proving to be cheaper than dressed stone which had been used in the past, but there were doubts about its lasting properties. It has however survived well, but so much undergrowth has now grown around the base as to make it difficult to get an unobstructed view of this attractive crossing. A small housing estate has been built in front, preventing access from that direction, and the land alongside is also private. The line that ran from Port Talbot to Pont-yr-hyl junction was closed in 1962. The total length of the viaduct is one hundred and fourteen yards (103m), and the height seventy three feet (22m) with forty foot (12m) arch spans.

Croeserw Viaduct, 864961 (170)

A stone viaduct with brick arches built, between 1886 and 1890, for the Rhondda and Swansea Bay Railway at Cymer Afan. There are seven arches covering a distance of one hundred and fifteen yards (105m), and it is sixty-five feet (20m) high. There is ample viewing from the road above, and the bridge is set in a pleasantly wooded section of the valley. The line has been closed since the late 1960s and the viaduct is by now showing signs of deterioration.

Carmarthenshire Railway and Tramway Bridges

Pwll-y-llygod Bridge, 446068 (159)

This unique single arch bridge was built around 1770 and carried a tramway over Afon Gwendraeth Fawr to connect with Kymer's Canal. Named after the nearby farm, it is considered to be the oldest tramway bridge in Wales. This information has been obtained from written sources, as it is regrettably on private land and cannot be viewed.

Tenby Viaduct, 129008 (158)

One of the lesser known viaducts, it is still worthy of note. It was built in 1866 and has seven round headed arches built of large rusticated blocks of limestone. It is still in use.

765902 (170)

A small low bridge, now serving as a footbridge between the car park and the shopping precinct in Port Talbot. It once carried the Rhondda and Swansea Bay line over Afon Afan. It has been restored, and is an interesting relic of the line.

Llandore Viaduct, 663958 (159)

The original viaduct was built by Brunel to carry the South Wales Line over Afon Tawe between 1847 and 1850. The track was carried on creosoted pine piles and was a third of a mile (530m) long, but all that remains of the original crossing are some of the masonry abutments.

The present viaduct was built in 1889, and is a metal structure supported by masonry piers. It is still in use and is an attractive structure when viewed from the reclaimed land downstream.

Neath River Rail Bridge, 729964 (170)

This bridge has the distinction of being the only swing bridge in the United Kingdom to have been built on a skew and also on a curve. Its length is three hundred and eighty-eight feet (118m), comprising of five sixty foot (18.2m) fixed spans, and a swing section of one hundred and sixty-seven feet (51m). The construction work began in 1892, after initial plans to build a tunnel under the river were abandoned. Securing the foundations proved to be a most difficult task, and was achieved by driving iron cylinders into the river bed and filling them with concrete.

It is still in use as a freight line, but there is no public access to it. The handsome iron structure, that carries the main South Wales line alongside the old road bridge, was built in 1906 to replace the original timber viaduct put up by Brunel.

Waungron Viaduct, 585025 (159)

Travellers along the M4 to the west of Swansea cannot fail to notice the impressive but crumbling brick viaduct over Afon Llwchwr *(Lougher)* between Junctions 47 and 48. It was built during the late 1840s to connect the South Wales Line to the Central Wales Railway that was being started from Llanelli. It is one of the earliest brick built viaducts, and was opened in 1852. It has eleven four centered arches, and is about eighty feet (24m) high.

897831 (170)

This is a small tramway bridge that was never adapted for any other use. It is surrounded by a housing estate at Abercynffig (*Aberkenfig*). It made the headlines in the local press during 1988 when it was threatened with demolition as part of a housing development. It was saved after a spirited protest which included a petition to the council. It dates from the 1820s and is a well built single arch bridge of dressed stone, which would suggest that it is the work of a skilled mason.

057834 (170)

This is a fine railway overbridge, built by the Barry Railway Co. over the road from Llantrisant to Pontypridd in 1889. A similar underbridge can be seen a little further north at 096865, but the one at 096809 has recently been demolished as part of a road widening scheme.

080927 (170)

This bridge was built in 1879 to carry the Taff Vale Line over Nant Clydach. The river flows under the centre arch, while the small arch at the northern end serves as a land arch, and the one at the southern end crosses the road.

A little higher up at Quakers Yard another fine stone bridge of three arches carries the line over Afon Taf. Both crossings are still in use.

077911 (170)

This is a lattice girder bridge supported on stone piers, with the letters T.V.R. (Taff Vale Railway) cut into sandstone blocks on top of the piers. It is situated just above Pontyberw, from which it is best viewed and is sometimes referred to by that name. The iron work is showing signs of rusting which will no doubt shorten its life, but it is still standing when most similar disused bridges have been demolished.

788924 (170)
Here is a bridge of three arches built in 1824 to carry a tramway from Bryn to Cwmafan. It can be found beyond a stretch of waste ground at the end of Hazlewood Terrace in Cwmafan. The parapet stones have gone, probably to provide stone for some local building, and have been replaced by concrete posts which serve no purpose whatsoever.

788898 (170)
A very attractive twin arch overbridge on the now defunct P.T.R. line, just above where Dyffryn Yard Depot once stood. The four layers of arch rings in decorative brickwork, as at Pont-yr-hyl, are worthy of note. It is sadly in a state of decay.

070900 (170)
This is a fine viaduct built in blue bricks just north of Pontypridd station. It was built between 1904 and 1907 during the extensive redevelopment of Pontypridd station, and replaced the original stone viaduct of a similar design built by Brunel for the Taff Vale Railway.

Quakers Yard Viaduct, 088965 (170)
This solid stone crossing over Afon Taf is among the few railway viaducts to have been widened. The earliest part of the construction was the work of Brunel in 1841, and carried only a single track. The development of the Taff Vale Railway was so rapid that it soon became necessary from the earlier, and this can still be seen. It straddles the Merthyr tramway track, and is best approached by walking along it from Quakers Yard.

Cwm Cwrelych Viaduct, 801065 (160)
Brunel, having to relent to the railway company's wishes, built timber viaducts over the Neath and Dulais rivers as a matter of economy, but was allowed to construct this fine stone bridge over Afon Cwrelych at Pont Walby near Glyn Neath. The line was built between 1846 and 1850, and once the temporary timber crossing at Aberdulais was completed, progress up the valley as far as Glyn Neath was swift. The long gradient up to Hirwaun was a different story, and it was 1848 before this viaduct had been completed. Originally there were five arches with a span of around forty-three feet each, built of red bricks and supported on

dressed stone piers. During the early years of the 20th century the southern arch was filled in, probably to strengthen the structure, and circular and rectangular openings were incorporated in the filling. The latter has since been bricked up, but the circular opening remains. The viaduct is a remarkable piece of engineering, its slender piers having been built as double arches, a rare feature on stone bridges, and the only one of its type to be seen on a railway viaduct in Wales.

The viaduct, which is sixty feet (18m) high, can be approached by a public footpath from the village, but the number of private houses that have been built in front, and one almost underneath, distract from what is an otherwise impressive structure.

171893 (171)

There are two railway girder underbridges just behind Bedwas church, with later stone parapets. The girders are well preserved, thanks to a coat of black tarry substance, and the words *Rhymney Railway 1863 Eagle Foundry Company Cardiff*, are clearly visible.

138861 (171)

This is a fine three arch viaduct carrying a minor road over the now dismantled Taffs Well to the Rhymney Valley line. Built in the late 1850s of dressed Pennant sandstone, it has since been repointed and remains in excellent condition.

A short distance below can be seen the blue brick piers of yet another of the Barry Railway girder bridges built at the same time as Pwll-y-pant.

Penydarren Tramway Bridges, 094962, 090965 (171)

These are two listed bridges of no special features, other than having been built to carry the tramway from Penydarren to Abercynon over Afon Taf. The one known as Greenfield Bridge replaced an earlier wooden structure which collapsed while a tram was crossing over it in 1815. The bridges are of some importance being among the largest of the early tramway crossings, one with a span of sixty-three feet (19m). They now carry a roadway.

Gellifelen Bridge, Clydach, 218121 (161)

This is a small but interesting bridge, built over a precipitous gorge to carry 'Bailey's Tramroad'. It was built around 1821 and is in some need of repair.

Crymlyn Viaduct

Pont Caerfyrddin
(Carmarthen Bridge) old print by W. Radclyffe

Pont y Bermo
(Barmouth Railway Bridge)

Cefncoed Viaduct

Pontsarn Viaduct

Pont-rhyd-y-fen Viaduct

Cynghordy Viaduct

Cefn Mawr Viaduct

84

Pont Gethin, Dyffryn Lledr
(Lledr Valley)

Chirk Aqueduct

Pontcysylltau Aqueduct

Conwy Tubular Bridge

The old Britannia Tubular bridge accross Afon Menai

Berriew (Aberriw) Aqueduct

Efyrnwy Aquaduct

Pont Morfa
(over Afon Tawe)

Newport Transporter bridge

Llangynidr bridge

Chain Bridge, Gwent

Monnow Bridge, Monmouth

Pontycafnau, Merthyr Tydfil

Chepstow Bridge

Iron inscription on Chepstow Bridge

Iron bridge at Robertstown, Aberdâr

Maesteg Iron Bridge

Smarts Bridge, Clydach Gorge

New Inn Bridge, Merthyr Mawr

Leckwith Bridge

The old bridge, Pontypridd

The Berw Bridge, Pontypridd

The new Berw Bridge, Pontypridd

Gofilon Bridge, 259133 (161)
Here is another bridge on 'Baileys Tramroad', spanning the deep Cwm Llanwenarth. Built around 1822, this is also badly in need of repair if it is to survive.

Nine Mile Point Bridge, Sirhywi, Wattsville, 203910 (171)
A fine arch over Afon Sirhywi, built around 1824 to carry the five mile long Penllwyn Tramway. It is now used to carry a footpath.

Pont Gam, Gelli-groes, 179942 (171)
This masonry arch bridge was also built to carry the Penllwyn Tramway, this time over Afon Ebwy *(Ebbw).*

Sgiwen *(Skewen),* 731969 (170)
This interesting listed bridge was built, in 1821, over the 'Tennant Canal' for the Royal copperworks.

Beaufort Bridge, 160115 (170)
This is a stone bridge built by John Hodgkinson in 1806 to replace an earlier timber structure which was condemned as dangerous two years earlier.

Pont y Doctor, 083892 (170)
This bridge has also been mentioned under road bridges, but prior to its widening it was part of a tramway that ran up the Rhondda Valley. A three arch stone structure, it was built in 1809 for Dr Richard Griffiths, a coal entrepreneur. At one time a weighing machine stood at one end which resulted in it also being called 'Machine Bridge'.

Stradey Bridge *(Pont Strade),* Llanelli 487011 (159)
This is a small cast iron bridge with the date 1845 and the words 'Waddle Lanmore' upside down in the arch. Waddle was the owner of the nearby Lanmore foundry. It was still in use in the early 1960s.

The Central Wales Railway

Cynghordy Viaduct, 808418 (147)

The Central Wales Line suffered more contracting problems than most, and although work started as early as the 1840s it progressed only in slow stages, and the line was not completed for twenty years. Of the numerous crossings there are two viaducts that are worthy of note, but they are situated in rather remote places.

The viaduct that towers above the small hamlet of Cynghordy near Llanymddyfri is a beautiful piece of railway construction. Aerial photographs emphasize the splendidly graceful curve which cannot be fully appreciated from ground level. The piers are of stone and the thirty-six foot (11m) wide arches, of which there are eighteen, are built of brick. The viaduct was completed in 1858.

One of the children of the contractor, Richard Hattersly, was killed during the construction of the seventh pier, and consequently it is said to be haunted. A chapel has been built almost underneath the ninety-three foot (28m) high viaduct.

Knucklas (Cnwclas) Viaduct, 248743 (148)

This viaduct took two years to build and was completed in 1862. At the time Knucklas was a small village of just a few houses, but recent development which has resulted in a number of modern homes being built underneath the viaduct has gone a long way to ruining its appearance. It is a spectacular and unusual construction, and the two castellated towers at either end were probably inspired by nearby Knucklas Castle, which was demolished to supply some of the stone.

There are thirteen arches, all constructed of stone spanning one hundred and ninety yards (172m). Each span is thirty-five feet (10.7m) and the line is sixty-nine feet (21m) above the river.

Llandeilo Railway Bridge

The railway criss-crosses Afon Tywi a number of times, mostly on lattice girder bridges of no great interest. But the one at Llandeilo has an unusual feature in that there are two fine stone-built arches on either side of the river. The standard method of construction prevails in the middle – with huge steel tubes sunk into the river bed to carry the girders. Therefore, it is something of a mystery why this method was not used throughout. The end result can hardly be described as an attractive bridge, but it is nevertheless noteworthy.

Railway Bridges of North-Eastern Wales

Firth Railway Viaduct, 284552 (117)

This five arch stone viaduct carried a railway line from Brymbo to Llanfynydd and was opened in 1872. The main traffic was in minerals, but it also carried passengers until 1950. It was finally closed in 1963. The viaduct is listed, but it is deteriorating badly.

Chirk (Y Waun) Railway Viaduct, 285376 (126)

The two major engineering achievements over Afon Ceiriog near Chirk are only feet apart. The railway viaduct is on the upstream side of the aqueduct, and was built by the Scotsman, Henry Robertson, to carry the Shrewsbury to Chester line. Building took place between 1846 and 1848. The railway viaduct has sixteen masonry arches, making it two hundred and eighty three yards (259m) long; it is some thirty feet (9m) higher than the aqueduct, at about one hundred feet (30m). The end arches replaced wooden ones in 1859. Both structures can be viewed from either side, and the railway viaduct is often used as an illegal vantage point for observing boats crossing the aqueduct. This is not to be encouraged since the viaduct is still in use.

Cefn Mawr Railway Viaduct, 285414 (126)

This viaduct is also known as Pentre viaduct, and is still in use carrying the Shrewsbury to Chester railway. The builder was again Henry Robertson and the work was completed in August 1848 when the M.P. Ormsby Gore keyed in the last stone in the final arch. There are nineteen arches in all, giving a total length of one thousand five hundred and eight feet (460m), with a maximum height of one hundred and forty feet (43m), making it the highest stone viaduct in the United Kingdom. This superb construction is also the longest viaduct in Wales, as well as being one of the first to be completed. Viewing this remarkable construction is an absolute must for anyone interested in bridges, and ample time should be allowed to examine it from all angles. The bridge is so long that the only way to do justice to it is to view from some distance away, from where the complete sweep across the valley can be seen at its best.

Llangollen Railway Viaduct, 208434 (117)

This is a large, solid looking stone viaduct consisting of six arches built in 1862 to carry the railway over Afon Dyfrdwy (Dee) just south of Pentrefelin. A section of the line is now open as a tourist attraction. The line is carried on iron girders resting on the stone pillars and the bridge sweeps in a gentle curve.

Hawarden Bridge, 302895 (117)
Hawarden Railway Bridge is a highly acclaimed piece of engineering, and is the largest bridge of its type in the world. Built in 1889, it consists of two bowed girder spans of one hundred and twenty feet (37m), and an opening span of one hundred and eighty-five feet (56m), swinging on one central pier. It is still in daily use, carrying the Wrexham to Chester line over the Dee estuary.

Cwm Prysor Railway Viaduct (124)
This superb nine arch viaduct, curving over Afon Prysor is a fitting memorial to one of the wildest stretches of line in North Wales – the Bala to Ffestiniog Railway. The first train passed over it in July 1882, some four months before the line was completed. It consists of brick arches on stone piers, and at its highest point is one hundred and five feet (32m) above the river. The arches have a span of twenty-five feet (7.6m).

It was finally closed, after much public protest, when part of the track was submerged under the Llyn Tryweryn in the early 1960s.

The section of the line from Trawsfynydd to Blaenau Ffestiniog was until recently in use, carrying nuclear waste from the power station at the Trawsfynydd. This line passes over another fine viaduct in the town of Blaenau Ffestiniog.

Pont Gethin, 779538 (115)
A fine stone railway viaduct built by Owain Gethin Jones, who also built Betws-y-coed railway station. It has been under threat for some time, as frequent demands are made to improve the road through Glyn Lledr *(valley),* but it is safe as long as British Rail maintain their link with Ffestiniog.

Pont Gethin is a superb example of Victorian railway architecture of an unusual design. Instead of constructing a number of arches of the same span, the designer decided on a stone embankment at both ends, with a tall but narrow arch for the roadway, and a long wide arch for the river crossing. Between the two are four small arches, and a number of castellated pilasters protrude from the parapets at strategic points along its length.

The large blocks of dressed stone that were used in the construction would suggest that its creator was influenced by the majestic Conwy road bridge in his design. Unless you are prepared to walk several miles along the narrow and busy road, described as the worst A class road in Britain, it is quite impossible to view the bridge, as there are no parking places along this stretch.

Gwynedd Tramway Bridges

Pont Afon Cegin, 592721

The bridge carried the Llandygái and Penrhyn railway over Afon Cegin during the first half of the 19th century. It also carried a roadway and may have been originally built for that purpose. It is a stone arch worthy of mention.

Pont Afon Gwyrfai, 480599 (115)

This is a bridge built for the Nantlle railway in 1827.

The Conwy and Britannia Tubular Bridges

The construction of a rail link from Chester to Holyhead became a matter of urgency in 1838, with the completion of the London to Liverpool railway line which resulted in the Irish Mail terminus being moved from Holyhead to Liverpool.

Robert Stevenson's plans for the railway were approved in 1842, but it was 1844 before the act was passed and work commenced on the line. The railway was built in sections and involved two major bridge constructions in Wales, those over Afon Conwy and the Menai Straits, as well as smaller ones over Afon Clwyd and Afon Clywedog.

Pont Conwy was attempted first, being the smaller of the two projects. It was looked upon as an experiment for the more ambitious crossing of the Menai.

Both bridges were designed by Francis Thomson. The one at Conwy was to harmonise with the castle, while Pont Britannia was to be a combination of Egyptian and Grecian styles. The towers for Pont Conwy were built of limestone from the Great Orme and Penmon Point, the latter source also being used for Pont Britannia. The massive blocks used in the construction of Pont Conwy weighed between five and eight tons each.

It was planned to float the tubes that were to carry the tracks down to the site at high water, a new technique that was to cause Stevenson considerable difficulty. The initial difficulties of raising the massive iron tubes, using steam lifting presses, were eventually overcome and the first was in position by March 1848.

While work on raising that second tube went ahead, trains used the first section and in August of that year Stevenson was involved in an accident that could have proved fatal. The lone carriage he was using to supervise the work was hit by an express, rendering him unconscious. One is left to wonder what the result on the project would have been had he not made a rapid recovery. The second tube was raised by October, and both were in position by the end of 1848, at the same time as the completion of the Anglesey section of the line. Holyhead was to regain the main contract with Ireland the same year. The railway link had reached the Menai Straits before the bridge that was to carry it over had been completed, and horses were used to haul waggons over the road bridge to connect with engines on either sides. A bridge built by Stevenson over Afon Dyfrdwy *(the Dee)*, based on the tubular principle, had recently collapsed while a train was crossing and doubts were being expressed about the safety of this type of structure. An inquiry took place but Stevenson weathered the storm, and work on erecting the Britannia tubes went ahead. This revolutionary design allowed for the expansion of the metal tubes by fixing them only at one end, and leaving the other free to move on rollers. The tubes that carried the line were lined with wood and rested on cast iron beams topped with putty. In the case of the Britannia Bridge, the load on the foundations was a collosal 29600 tons.

The bridge was named after the Britannia rock on which the centre pier stood. The four centre tubes of four hundred and sixty feet (140m) each, were one hundred and five feet (32m) above high water, the height stipulated by the Admiralty. The four side tubes were two hundred and fifty feet (76m) long, and the Britannia tower was one hundred and seventy one feet (52m) high and the walls were eight to ten feet (2.4 to 3m) thick and filled with masonry.

There were plans to install a figure of Britannia on top of this tower but it was abandoned when the company went through a period of financial crisis.

Four giant lions, two each side, were carved in limestone by John Thomas, who had also worked on the Houses of Parliament at the time. They weighed thirty tons each, and were thirty-five feet (10.7m) high and twelve feet (3.6m) wide. They even inspired a Welsh rhyme,

Dau lew tew, dau ochor yma, dau ochor drew.
(Two fat lions, two this side, two on the other.)

There was no official opening ceremony, but Queen Victoria and Prince Albert, with the young Prince of Wales, visited the bridge in 1849 and were given a tour of inspection by Stevenson.

The first train across in March 1850 was driven by Stevenson himself, partly to allay fears that the tubes would collapse. The bridge had cost six hundred and seventy thousand pounds, three times the estimated budget. It took four years to complete and cost nineteen lives. It was not the same bridge as had been planned, which was intended to be of two arches one hundred and five feet (32m) above the water. This was abandoned because fears had been expressed that sailing ships might collide with the spandrels.

On a windy evening in May 1970 the wooden lining caught fire, and the bridge was soon ablaze from end to end. Fire engines and television film crews rushed to the scene, and a shocked nation watched the destruction of one of its landmarks on the evening news.

The cause was never firmly established, although sabotage was suspected but not proven. There were fears that the rail link with the island would be closed for good, but repairs were eventually carried out, using an open track with a roadway on top, which provided Anglesey with a badly needed second road crossing.

The only stone river crossings on the Welsh section of the Chester to Holyhead line was a viaduct at Old Colwyn and a similar one at Llanddulas. The latter was washed away in 1879 when a freak flood undermined the foundations, and a new bridge of girders supported on seven stone pillars was built. The length was two hundred and twenty-four feet (68m), with a span of thirty-two feet (9.7m) between pillars.

The Llangollen Canal

The Llangollen branch was one of a system of canals between Afon Hafren *(the Severn)* in the south and the Mersey in the north. It was an ambitious project built during the canal mania of the last decade of the 18th century. By the early 1850s the Shrewsbury to Chester railway had been completed and further extensions to the canal did not materialise. Originally intended as an agricultural canal, it soon became important in the industrial development of the area.

The entire system was known as the Ellesmere canal, and Llangollen was the name given to the section between Welsh Frankton in Shropshire and the Horseshoe Fall weir at Llandysilio, where it was supplied with water from Afon Dyfrdwy *(the River Dee)*. The name only became established after the Act of 1944, which gave permission to close large sections of local canals. Llangollen was included in the original closure, but was reprieved in 1954 because it supplied mid and north-eastern Cheshire with much of its water.

The canal does not cross the border into Wales until it reaches the vicinity of Chirk, but the short distance, between that point and Llangollen has a number of bridges, including the two most spectacular aqueducts in Wales at Chirk and Pontcysylltau.

Most of the bridges were of the standard hump back type, and with many brickworks scattered about north-eastern Wales, brick was often used in preference to stone. The building procedure was simple enough. A flat horizontal base was formed below water level and the arch, consisting of a single layer of bricks placed lengthwise at right angles to the arch, was covered with rubble. A brick parapet was added, with stone coping. The arches were narrow, allowing only one boat to pass through at a time. The abutments, or 'wing walls' as they were known, were parallel at first to accommodate the iron grooves for the stop planks that sealed off a section in the event of a leakage. Further on they would sweep outwards, until the canal was wide enough for two boats to pass each other.

In the early 1950s there were forty-nine bridges between Welsh Frankton and Llandysilio, but some have since disappeared, while others have been levelled off using steel girders. All the bridges are named as well as numbered. Starting at the bridge before Chirk aqueduct which is No. 20, and named Monks Bridge. The others of interest are: No. 27, Irish Bridge (probably refers to the builders); No. 28, just before the Pontcysylltau aqueduct was known as the Fron lift up Bridge; No. 32 was a roving timber bridge; and No. 33, White Bridge was a footbridge.

The following, although some are of no great interest, are near the road and can be seen while driving or walking between Pontcysylltau and Llangollen:

No. 34, Plas y Pentre (262414); No. 35, Millers Bridge (258413); No. 36, Bryn Ceirch (255413); No. 37, Plas Isaf (253414); No. 38 Bryn Hywel (250418); No. 40, Plas Ifan (247422); No. 41, Sun Trefor Bridge (242424); No. 43, Llandyn 1 (232246); No. 44, Llandyn 2 (227423); and No. 46, Pen-y-ddôl (211426).

Aqueducts of North-Eastern Wales

Chirk Aqueduct, 287372 (126)

The two aqueducts on the Llangollen canal were built by Thomas Telford. They are without doubt the finest aqueducts in Wales, and yet are so different in construction that one cannot help thinking Telford was playing safe with the traditional heavy piers on the Chirk, before embarking on the slender elegant design of Pontcysylltau. The ten arches are six hundred feet (183m) long and carry the canal seventy feet (21.5m) above Afon Ceiriog. The water channel is eleven feet (3.3m) wide, with six foot (0.6m) high masonry sides. The troughs were of a revolutionary design, using iron platings with hollow spandrels to the arches. In the event of a leakage, water could escape without placing unacceptable strain on the masonry.

The work was completed in 1801 and the original troughs were replaced in the 1870s. The viaduct is now overshadowed by the taller railway crossing, which serves as an unofficial but admirable viewpoint to watch the transport on the canal. Colt Hoare has left us a fine sketch of the aqueduct under construction, and Gastineaus' print from his *Wales Illustrated* depicts it before the railway viaduct ruined the view from the eastern side.

Pontcysylltau Aqueduct, 271420 (117)

This masterpiece of engineering is possibly the finest aqueduct in Britain. It is only a short distance away from the one at Chirk, and had been under construction for six years when Chirk was completed. Work commenced in 1795, and it was not completed until 1805.

The original plan was for a much smaller crossing of Afon Dyfrdwy *(River Dee)* coupled with a series of locks, but this was abandoned in favour of this elegant and controversial design. Telford was assisted by William Jessop, who played an important role but received little credit for his work. Telford claimed that he had the sole responsibility for the project, a claim much refuted by Jessop and which cast a cloud over the success of the venture. The construction called for nineteen sets of arches, each with a fifty-three foot (13m) span. Each pillar was solid at the base, but hollow from about seventy feet (21.5m) upwards. The slender piers carry the iron trough for a distance of one thousand and seven feet (307m) and a height above the river bed of one hundred and twenty-seven feet (38.7m).

The construction faced immense problems. The fast flowing river made it difficult to place coffer dams around the foundation sites, and to haul and place large blocks of stone in position at a height of over a hundred feet (30m) would have been daunting to say the least. Ox blood was mixed with the mortar for the joints, which must have resulted in the contractor having a standing order with the slaughter houses for miles around.

The canal is in constant use during the summer months, with a stream of pleasure craft crossing the aqueduct regularly. There is a towpath with railings on one side, but for those travelling in a barge the other side offers a sheer drop, and is not to be recommended to anyone suffering from vertigo.

Icing during extremely cold weather can cause cracking in cast iron troughs due to expansion, but the designers overcame this problem by installing plugs that allowed sections to be isolated and drained. When it becomes necessary to drain the entire trough during maintenance, a crowd of onlookers can be expected because the sight of the water gushing down into the river below is an amazing spectacle in itself.

It is best to approach the Aqueduct from the Trefor side, and the walk across the towpath is an exhilarating experience for those with a head for heights.

Clwyd Bridges

Pontcysylltau, 269420 (117)

The road bridge is a little upstream of the Aqueduct and provides a splendid viewing point from below. Llwyd called it 'Pont Kyssylhie', but gives no further details. It appears to have been built in 1697 according to the date on one of the downstream cutwaters. It does not appear to have been widened, as it is still only ten feet (3m) wide, there have been a great many repairs.

Jervoise describes it as having:

> three segmental arches with double arch rings built in two orders and small keystones which project slightly.

He also states that it is fifty-three yards (50m) long.

The Montgomeryshire Canal

The Montgomeryshire canal, set among the steep wooded hills and rich pastures of Dyffryn Hafren *(the Severn valley)*, is among the most beautiful of the Welsh Canals. The main object of the canal was to carry lime to farms from the vast quarries on Llanymynech Hill, and to provide the large estates in Dyffryn Hafren with a dependable means of transport. The canal was built in several stages and over a long period of time because capital frequently ran out. The original eastern section was started in 1794, and taken as far as Guilsford by 1797. It was only with the renewed interest in canal building that took place around 1815 that the western branch was built, and this did not reach Newtown until 1821, due largely to the trouble in building the Aqueducts.

Aqueducts

The canal crosses two main rivers and three large streams, and these aqueducts had to be rebuilt during the early 19th century.

Aberbechan Aqueduct, 143935 (136)

This small three arch aqueduct was designed by Josias Jessop and built by John Williams during the construction period of 1815 to 1829. By 1859 it was in need of replacing, and although there were plans to replace it with a cast iron trough like the ones at Brithdir and Welshpool, it was repaired in stone and promptly collapsed again. The result of the collapse is still evident today; the upstream face bulges outwards, and only the southernmost of the three arches retains the original stonework. The others have been repaired in blue bricks. It is an attractive little construction despite the repairs and can be seen from the towpath.

Berriew (Aberriw) Aqueduct, 188006 (136)

The first attempt to construct this aqueduct over Afon Rhiw, by John Bedford in 1796, collapsed almost as soon as it was built. The next attempt was in need of repair by 1889 when it was rebuilt using blue engineering bricks. A plaque on the downstream face reads 'Restored 1889', and the iron railings were also installed at this time.

The aqueduct has two river arches flanked by two smaller road arches, which are a tight squeeze for anything other than light vehicles. It was piped in 1948 but the water channel has recently been replaced. The stonework rests on timber baulks which themselves rest on stakes driven into the river bed, an early engineering method also found in some road bridges.

Welshpool Aqueduct (Nant Lledan), 227074 (126)

The present aqueduct was constructed by J.A.S. Sword in 1836 to replace the original crumbling stone structure. The water is carried in an iron trough, flanked by paths supported on masonry arches. The cast iron railings are particularly fine, and a good viewing point is from the railway girder bridge on the upstream side. A plaque recording its construction can be seen above the arch.

Brithdir Aqueduct, 197022 (136)

The massive iron trough that forms the present aqueduct was used by G.W. Buck to replace the original stone trough in 1819. A similar design was used by Sword at Welshpool when he took over the engineers post from Buck. The massive weight of the metal and water on the abutments caused subsidence, which required them to be partly rebuilt in 1890. The ornamental cast iron railings on the tow path side are of the same type as those found on canals on which Thomas Telford was the engineer, and it is possible that these, and all the other cast iron used, came from the Plaskynaston Foundry at Pontcysylltau.

Carreghorfa Aqueduct, 259206 (126)

This aqueduct was built in the 1860s to carry the canal over the West Shropshire Mineral Line. It is made of riveted wrought iron plates, supported on cast iron columns.

The Efyrnwy Aqueduct, 253196 (126)

The largest aqueduct on the canal, this is also the most interesting. It is a five arch construction made of stone, and has caused more problems than all the other aqueducts. It was started under the supervision of John Dartford during the 1790s. Dartford had a number of canal contracts at the time, putting him under considerable pressure. The foundations proved to be insufficient to withstand the weight of the stone arches and the heavy core of puddling clay, and this in conjunction with John Dartford's inexperience as a bridge builder put the whole project in considerable jeopardy. When an arch collapsed during construction, Dartford resigned and went to America, leaving his brother Thomas to clear up the mess. Thomas Dartford's effort had sprung a leak by 1823, and every arch had cracked. A report to the shareholders recorded that it was 'ill built of bad materials'. An attempt to cure the leaks by repuddling the channel caused further stress on the arches, and the walls bulged alarmingly. The extensive reinforcement programme included the insertion of red hot ties through the structure, which are still visible.

Further drastic measures were required in 1892, when the unstable masonry of the distorted central walling was held in place by a number of *fish bellied* cast iron beams.

The aqueduct has also coped with the constant battering of large trees carried by floodwater, which often lodged on the upstream face. The original triangular cutwaters have been replaced by hammer dressed masonry, and similar alterations can be seen on the aqueducts at Aberbechan and Berriew.

The original parapets were probably made of wood, and the iron railings were installed by G.W. Buck in 1828. The stone supports resemble miniature Egyptian style Temple Pylons.

The Efyrnwy Flood Aqueducts

There are two large flood aqueducts built into the embankment on either side of the river crossing. The southern aqueduct of three arches has been refaced with blue bricks. The northern aqueduct has four arches, and has also probably been rebuilt, but using some of the original stone. They are bulky constructions, and are more like tunnels through the embankment than separately built aqueducts.

They can be reached by walking along the towpath from the B4398. The walk from Carreghorfa Locks to the aqueduct and back is under a mile (1.6km), and well recommended.

Pont Cynon – Bacon drawing circ. 1820–30, by local permission of Aberdare Library.

114

Montgomeryshire Canal Bridges

There are a number of interesting bridges to be seen on the canal. Many of the original stone structures were replaced by iron girder types by G.W. Buck during the first two decades of the 19th century. Buck was considered to be 'iron mad', but cast iron, being weak in tension, will snap under heavy loading, and was by no means as effective for bridges as wrought iron and steel. In order to overcome this weakness, a 'fish bellied' design was used giving greater thickness in the middle of the beam. There are six surviving bridges of this type on the canal, one of the oldest being Pont Pentreheulyn (No. 97). In some cases dismantled beams have been reused, as at Aberbechan.

The iron beam bridge at Aberbechan (No. 152) was a modest construction by Thomas Penson, before he built Pont Brynderwen in 1853. The casting for Pont Aberbechan, as for Brynderwen, occurred at Brymbo Ironworks, and a dated plaque records the event.

Pont Glanhafren (No. 143) is an ornate blue brick structure, resting on flat iron beams cast in 1880. There are two lifting bridges of interest north of Welshpool which are steel replacements for earlier timber structures. These are known as Abbey Bridge (No. 112) and Moors Farm Bridge (No. 114).

There is an elegant turn bridge south of Garthmyl (No. 142), as also is No. 144. They probably date from around 1850.

The bridge enthusiast is often unaware of the enormous number, and variety, of bridges that were built over inland waterways, because they are seldom seen by anyone other than canal travellers and walkers of towpaths. For the historian, the almost total lack of modernisation since their completion make them worthy of examination.

There are two basic types; the fixed bridge, and the moveable bridge. The latter are mostly found across navigable rivers, and are often huge masterpieces of Victorian engineering skills. The only two in Wales in this category are Pont y Bermo and Neath Railway Bridge, both of which are over estuaries rather than canals. There are several small moveable bridges over the three main canal sections, some of which are modern replacements.

The most common type of fixed bridge found in Wales is the single arch, hump back type, built to carry minor roads or to serve as agricultural access. These bridges, known as accommodation crossings, were constructed to enable farmers to move livestock over the canal, and often no road or track leads to them. Although marked as thin lines on the O.S. Maps they are often difficult to reach, and unless one is a barge devotee, it will involve long walks along the towpath.

When the towpath has been well maintained such a walk can be pleasant, but far too often it is a hard slog through a mass of undergrowth, and when the bridge is eventually reached it is often little more than a curious shape festooned with ivy. Close examination will sometimes reveal well built and very attractive bridges.

These bridges are seldom wider than what was necessary to accommodate a horse and cart.

The main building material used in the south and east of Wales was stone, and brick in the north-east. The abutments would generally be left hollow, and filled with earth or rubble of which there was no shortage. The towpath usually went under the bridge, and on busy sections the tow rope would cause considerable wear to the side of the arch. Over a period of time these developed sharp edges, and in some cases cast iron plates were fixed to the sides to prevent the rope from chaffing.

It was a common practice on some canals to whitewash the bridges and the centre of the arch was marked with a stripe as a navigational aid. This was useful to those steering dimly lit boats at night.

In the event of a bridge opening being too narrow to allow a footpath, the horse would be unhitched, walked over to the other side, and the tow rope reconnected. Sometimes a narrow arch or tunnel would be cut through the bridge abutment to allow the horse through.

When a towpath switched from one bank to another, a construction known as a turnover or roving bridge was used. The towpath would mount the bridge and cross over it, before descending to the canal edge on the opposite bank. The horse could then proceed along the towpath, and under the bridge, without having to unhitch the towrope. Moveable canal bridges are necessary when a roadway crosses the water. A well known type of bridge used for this purpose is a bascule bridge, and a number of these bridges can be found on the Llangollen canal. The method of opening, which had to be carried out by the bargee, involved pulling a chain which raised the bridge. In some cases he had to provide the rope and a bridge at Pontcysylltau carries the inscription: 'Cast a rope over the beam to open bridge'. There is a modern bascule at Talybont on the Brecon Canal.

Many of the Welsh canal bridges, on both restored and neglected sections, are pleasant but unremarkable, with just the odd gem worthy of special attention. A wide range of construction methods can be found along the same section of a canal. Although the main contract was carried out by a large firm, bridges were often sub-contracted to local builders who stamped their own building methods on them.

Unlike road bridges those over canals seldom have names and are referred to by a number, starting from a junction and working outwards. The Towpath Guides describe the canal bridges in detail; No. 6 on the Llangollen Canal is referred to as 'a curved roving bridge'. In order to make towing easier on difficult sections, some bridges were built on a skew. A fine example can be seen at Aberdulais Basin on the Neath Canal.

The Welsh canals are well documented and any serious bridge observer should consult the towpath guides.

The Brecon, Abergavenny and Monmouth Canals

Most of the canals in South Wales were built during the last decade of the 18th century to transport iron and coal to the ports. The Brecon and Abergavenny canal, however, was originally used to carry lime, manure and farm produce, and only carried iron from Gilwern after being connected to the Monmouth canal during the repair of Pont-y-moel aqueduct (over Afon Lwyd) in 1812. The route for the Brecon and Abergavenny canal was surveyed by Thomas Dartford in 1792; construction started in 1794, and the canal reached Brecon in 1800.

There are one hundred and sixty-six bridges and aqueducts on the two canals, the last number being allocated to Gasworks Bridge in Brecon (Aberhonddu). The bridge numbers are recorded on cast iron plates on the 'down-side' of the bridges, and some are referred to by name.

Brynych Aqueduct

This is the most interesting aqueduct on the canal, and crosses Afon Wysg *(River Usk)* two miles from Brecon. It was built by Thomas Dartford in 1800 and is similar to the one he built over Afon Efyrnwy as part of the Montgomery Canal. It is a massive masonry structure of four arches, with a twelve foot (3.6m) wide channel which is lined with puddled clay. The siting of the aqueduct determined the position of the nearby lock, which kept the height of the aqueduct to a minimum. Dartford was fortunate with his foundations because Brynych never needed the massive repairs that were to blight the similar canals on the Montgomery Canal.

Talybont Bascule Bridge

The present bridge was built in 1970 to replace a fixed timber crossing, in order to allow boats to reach Brecon. It is now electrically controlled.

There are a variety of bridges along the canal, constructed from different materials, built or rebuilt at different times, and differing in use. Number 162 is a roving bridge while Number 161 is badly distorted and has been braced using iron arches. Storehouse Bridge (No. 158) was rebuilt in 1958, while Almshouse Bridge (No. 148) was rebuilt in 1962. Number 155 is a new drawbridge that has been built to Dartford's original design. The B4558 follows the canal, crossing it a number of times. Some of the resulting bridges are modern, but some of the oldest on the canal are to be found between Gofilon and Brecon. They are often narrow and humpbacked, the best being Number 163 at Brynych, Number 131 at Llangynidr, and Number 97 at Gofilon.

The Neath and Tennant Canal

The Neath and Tennant canals were built separately, work beginning on the Neath section in 1792, and completed in 1795. The twelve mile (19km) waterway transported coal, lime, iron and even gunpowder, from works further up the Neath valley to the docks at Britton Ferry.

The Tennant Canal was completed in 1824, connecting the Neath Canal at Aberdulais Basin with Port Tennant near Swansea. The Tennants eight and a half miles (13.7km) makes it the second longest privately built canal in Britain. The Neath and Tennant Preservation Society have restored a number of sections, and the towpaths make a pleasant walk.

Aberdulais Aqueduct, 774994 (170)
The aqueduct that carries the Tennant Canal over Afon Nedd *(River Neath)* is a low stone construction and was completed in 1824. All of its ten arches are in good condition, and the channel retains water with few leaks. When the canal was in its heyday funeral processions were charged a penny to cross, which speaks ill of the condition of the roads at the time. The Basin is a popular attraction and a base for energetic walkers who can follow the towpath to the next Aqueduct near Clyne *(Y Clun)*.

Ynysbwllog Aqueduct, 803011 (170)
This aqueduct near the village of Y Clun *(Clyne)* is similar in construction to the one at Aberdulais, although it is some thirty years older. Up until 1980 it had six fine arches and was almost intact until a flood washed away a pier, resulting in the collapse of two of the arches. The water is now carried in a large iron pipe, and is sufficient to supply the canal below which has not been restored and is little more than a waterlogged ditch. The two ends have been sealed off with iron railings, but it is still a dangerous place and care is required. It was sketched by Wood in 1811. At the time there was no bridge at Resolfen, and the tow path provided the only crossing of the river.

Clydach Aqueduct, Neath Abbey, 738972 (170)
This is a small twin arch aqueduct that is all but buried in the bed of Afon Clydach. It was built in 1821.

There are three fine cast iron aqueducts on the Neath Canal, all of which are listed. They were probably cast at Neath Abbey ironworks in the 1930s to replace earlier stone ones. They are to be found at Aberpergwm

(863058); Resolfen (827031); and Rheola (842039). The latter is considered to be the finest, the two side panels having eleven Tuscan columns cast into them, and the deck is of eight cast plates.

Bridges

Most of the bridges over the canal are of the basic type but two are more interesting. The one at Aberdulais basin, known as Pont-gam, is a fine example of a skew bridge, and the one west of Neath Abbey Aqueduct has parapets formed out of cast blocks of copper slag.

Pont Morfa 664954 (159)

This is an iron and timber bascule bridge built in 1909 over Afon Tawe to carry waste from Morfa works to the waste tips on the eastern side of the river. Originally raised by hydraulics, it is now fixed. A new timber decking roadway has been laid over the top which can take wheeled vehicles, but it is mainly used by pedestrians visiting the sports centre on the other side of the river.

The hazard of debris coming downriver with a flood has been successfully averted by positioning some timber rails in the river bed, diverting any large floating obstacles under the metal section. The overall length of the bridge is about seventy yards (64m) and the present roadway is eighteen feet (3.3m) wide.

The Swansea Canal

Little remains of the Swansea Canal. Most of the channel has been filled in and used for road construction, the only section that still holds water being the section that passes through Clydach and Pontardawe.

Ystalyfera Aqueduct, 772092 (160)

This, the largest aqueduct on the canal, has through some miracle survived. It was built by Thomas Sheasby in the mid 1790s, and was among the first aqueducts in Britain to use mortar instead of puddling clay as a waterproofing agent. It consists of three segmental arches built on top of a feeder weir. The large culvert at the northern end supplied water to a fulling mill at Y Gurnos.

Bridges of Dyffryn Wysg *(Usk Valley)*

Afon Wysg *(Usk)* rises on the northern slopes of the Black Mountains and by the time it has reached the Sea at Newport, it has been crossed by a wider range of bridges than any other river in South Wales. A tempestuous river when in flood, it had no respect for the earlier flimsy wooden bridges thrown across it, as Leyland records that 'Uske Bridge at Brekenoc was thrown down by rage of Uske water', in 1535. But most of the 17th and 18th century stone bridges have surprisingly survived with only a little rebuilding. These include the almost untouched bridge at Llangynidr and the thirteen arch Crickhowell *(Crucywel)* crossing, one of the longest stone bridges in Wales.

The famous bridge building family, the Edwards' of Pontypridd, left their mark and even if William Edwards had his earlier bridge at Usk sandwiched between later widenings, his son David has left a superb example of his building technique at Tredunnock.

Newport Transporter Bridge, 318862 (171)
This unique metal construction, built in 1906 by F. Arnedin to carry both freight and foot passengers over Afon Wysg at Newport Docks, was an extravagant project that failed to achieve its full potential. The only other similar bridge in the United Kingdom is at Middlesborough, and there are a further two in Europe.

The travelling roadway is suspended from cables, stretched between two lattice steel towers, two hundred and forty-two feet (74m) high, which can be seen for miles around. The bridge has been out of commission for some years and it is unlikely that the local authorities will be able to acquire sufficient funds to carry out the necessary repairs. The span is six hundred and forty-five feet (196.5m), and five hundred and ninety-two feet (180.5m) between the towers. It has gained something of a macabre reputation in being a notorious suicide spot.

Pont Caerleon, 333912 (171)
The Romans built an important fortress in the vicinity of Caerleon, and there has been much speculation that they crossed Afon Wysg by means of a stone bridge, but no remains have been discovered. One of the first references to a bridge here was when one Nigel Chepstow left money towards its maintenance in 1387. It was without doubt a wooden structure, similar to the one described by Leyland in the 16th century. Early in the 19th century E. Donovan describes a most unusual wooden bridge, designed so that in times of flood the roadway would rise rather

than be washed away. It appears that it was never put to the test because floodwater failed to reach the platform.

William Coxe in 1801 noted that a new bridge of stone is in contemplation, but it was a few years before the magistrates finally accepted a suitable design. The stone bridge was completed by 1812 and was depicted by J.C. Wood as having three semicircular arches. However within a year it was found to be in need of 'immediate repair', and the expense was deducted from the amount still owed to the builder.

The bridge has a difficult approach, and with the arrival of motor driven transport, accidents were inevitable. One such mishap occurred in 1914 when an army vehicle skidded through the southern parapet and hung suspended over the river, resulting in the closure of the bridge until it could be removed.

In 1974 the footpaths were removed to ease the flow of traffic, and an iron pedestrian crossing was erected over the northern cutwaters. This resulted in the full twenty-two foot (6.7m) width being available to traffic. Those who now risk life and limb to study the plaque set into the parapet will find that only the top half is still legible. It was not mentioned by Jervoise for the good reason that it was not there at the time, having been inserted into the masonry in 1956 at the insistence of a local historian who had discovered it among a pile of stones outside the Legionary Museum, and having been unable to discover any records of the bridge, he convinced the Council that it was the original foundation stone.

The inscription reads,

This bridge was erected at the expense of the County by David Edwards and his two sons William and Thomas. Completed MDCCC.

It was later discovered that this plaque had no connection with the bridge, and was removed from Newport bridge when it was taken down in 1927. Jervoise in his description of Newport Bridge states that it had a plaque with exactly the same inscription.

Caerleon bridge was actually built by a Mr Hodgkinson and designed by a Mr Jessop. Although it was repaired in 1956 and again when the footway was built in 1974, the arches have, as Jervoise recorded in 1932, 'suffered little alteration since it was built'.

Pont Gwenllian, 852284 (160)
This bridge was constructed in 1833 and is often considered to be one of the finest on the upper stretches of the river. There was a 'Pont Gwenllian Howell' somewhere in the vicinity in 1725 which, according to

documents in Brecon Museum, was then described to be 'ancient'. Who this particular lady was we do not know for certain, but she must have been of some social standing to have a bridge named in her honour.

The present Pont Gwenllian is a superb construction of old red sandstone and was designed by W. Watkins the County Surveyor and built by Thomas Price of Llangamarch. The two abutments are built on solid rock which has contributed to its excellent state of repair, although the fine stonework is becoming increasingly obliterated by lichen. The arch has a span of thirty feet (9.1m), and it features attractive voussoirs and a string course, although the latter is slightly out of line.

The fact that two roads join on the bridge itself has resulted in the need for large wing-walls, which add to its charm. At one time it was the first bridge over the Usk river, and was built on the old turnpike roads from Trescastell to Llandeilio Fawr and Llanddeusant. It is not easy to find but well worth the effort. Viewing, particularly in summer when the surrounding trees are in full leaf is rather difficult.

Pont Nant Brân, 986294 (160)

This small single arch bridge over Nant Brân, close to the mill, has all the appearance of an ancient pack horse crossing, but its twisted arch resulted from poor building techniques since it is probably little more than one hundred and fifty years old. Jervoise did not consider it of any great importance and only recorded the specifications; eleven yards (10m) long and eight and a half feet (2.5m) wide, with stones set on edge serving as parapets.

The present structure however has all the appearance of being rebuilt, possibly since the time Jervoise recorded it. The width is now only just over six feet (1.8m) and there are no parapet stones. The cobbled roadway has been relaid, or at least repointed, and the abutments strengthened with concrete, but it is still worth a visit. It can be viewed from all points and as one would expect, the tract over it is restricted to pedestrians.

Pont Aber Brân, 987292 (160)

There was mention of a bridge over Afon Wysg at Aber Brân as early as 1687, but the present crossing is credited to James Parry of Hay who, according to the plaque on the upstream parapet, which is now almost illegible, built it in 1791. It reads *Erected MDCCXCI by James Parry*, but Jervoise considered that it had been rebuilt in 1854. There are indications that it has undergone repairs since then; the upstream cutwaters appear to be recent, and the parapet is repointed. It has three semicircular arches and the four recesses, also semicircular in shape, each have a stone seat. The upstream side supports a rusty sewer pipe, and it is therefore best viewed from downstream. Jervoise records it as being twelve feet (3.6m) wide and thirty-one yards (28.3) long.

Pont Abersefin 972288 and Pont Abercamlas 965291 (160)

These two bridges, only a short distance apart, are without doubt the most important bridges on the Upper Usk. Both are listed, but it is very regrettable that they are on private land and cannot be viewed. There is little information available, but they could be from as early as the mid 17th century.

In the case of Pont Abersefin, a wooden sign with flaking paint makes it clear that it is a private drive and you enter at your peril. Part of the bridge can be seen from the A40 trunk road when the trees are bare. It appears to have four arches of rugged, moss covered, stone construction.

Pont Abercamlas is an impressive structure of three arches and smaller land openings, and is built of red sandstone. The sign says No Through Road, and it leads only to the estate. Do not be tempted to walk down it as I did for a quick look, for your presence will not be welcome. It was built around 1660.

It is interesting to note that Jervoise did not mention these bridges, although he must have been aware of them. It is possible that he was refused permission to record them, or bearing in mind the attitude of land owners towards historians at that time, he might not have made any attempt to see them.

Pont Llwyncynefin 926292 (160)

The bridge was originally a private crossing for a mansion of that name. It has two arches featuring attractive double rings and a span of twenty eight yards (25.6m) and a width of only nine feet.

Described by Jervoise as 'a very attractive bridge' on the road from Senni Bridge to Llandeilo'r-fân, Pont Llwyn Cynefin has absorbed some repair work without losing any of its character. The recesses are round, the downstream one having been repaired and in the process losing its seat. A plaque in the upstream recess states, *P.H.E. 1750 E,T. T.W. Masons. I Gwyn*, The remainder is illegible.

Pont Caniedydd 039244 (160)

This is a well built and attractive little bridge that lacks any significant features. It was mentioned in the Sessions of 1711 as 'Pont Cynheddydd', and the name change, for whatever reason, came about towards the end of the 19th century. It is unlikely that the present structure dates from 1711, for it does not appear to have undergone much alteration, apart from the recent replacement of most of the parapet stones. One of the two segmental arches is almost completely silted up, serving only as a flood opening. The road that it carries over Nant Sere is narrow, although the width between the parapets is a generous twelve feet (3.6m). There is a welcome parking space for a few cars nearby, provided for the benefit of hikers who can visit the waterfalls further up the wooded valley from here. The two next bridges lower down, Cantref and Lower Cantref, are modern by comparison. Pont y Felindre, the last one on Afon Cynrig, was described by Jervoise as 'a massive structure'. Sometime between then and now it has been destroyed and replaced by an ugly concrete construction.

Lock Bridge 077273 (160)
This massive bridge over Afon Wysg, so named because of its proximity to one of the canal locks, is reputed to have been built in 1773, but the present structure appears to be more modern. There are four arches in all with a recess over each cutwater. The total span is sixty-eight yards (63m), with a width of eighteen feet (5.4m). The land below the bridge is private and the best viewpoint is from the 'Brynych Aqueduct' a short distance upstream.

Usk Bridge Brecon *(Pont-ar-Wysg, Aberhonddu)* 044286 (160)
John Leyland mentions a bridge at Brecon that had been destroyed by a flood in 1535 which had been caused by melting snow. This bridge was probably a wooden structure and the first stone structure appears to have been built in 1563. The actual date is in some doubt and is arrived at by translating and calculating an old Welsh stanza,

> *Mil oedd oedran Iesu moliant*
> *Trugain a thri mwy na phumcant,*
> *Y gnawd peth difethiant,*
> *Pont ar Wysc mi rho gof i gant.*

It states that a thousand years after Christ plus sixty and three more than five hundred hundreds will recollect a bridge on the Usk. It must have been an impressive structure for Thomas Churchyard the 16th century poet writes,

> The river Oske, and Hondie runnes thereby,
> Fouer bridges good, of stone stands one each stream,
> The greatest bridge, doth to the colledge lye.

An illustration by John Ogilby in 1675 indicates a bridge of seven arches, and two extra were added at the Llanfaes end during the repair work of 1794.

It is not well known that the repairs of 1794 were carried out by Thomas Edwards, one of the family of William Edwards of Pontypridd fame. The work cost a thousand pounds, and involved the removal of a smithy, for which Richard Balcot was compensated four guineas (£1.10).

Thomas Edwards had contracted to maintain the bridge for seven yeas, but had died before the time was up, and when further repairs were required in 1801 his widow agreed to honour the contract although she was of the opinion that the time had expired. Her settlement of one hundred and fifty pounds was a shrewd move, for the repairs to the bridge cost over four hundred pounds.

The repairs were carried out by John Maud a respected builder who agreed to maintain the bridge for twenty-one years. He was to be paid five guineas, (£5.25) annually, but the bridge was to be inspected before the money was handed over.

Brecon Bridge is reputed to have been built in 1563. In his *History of Breconshire* published in 1809, Theophilus Jones mentions that 'two waggons may now, with ease repass each other', but the bridge was in constant need of repair. In the early 1930s Jervoise records that work was in progress 'to strengthen the foundations of the piers on the upstream side'. He goes on to mention that it had seven arches, a total length of eighty-four yards (77m), was twenty-two feet (6.7m) wide between the parapets.

Since that time there have been considerable additions to the bridge in the form of iron footways, and other rebuilding and general improvements. Although the arches remain, most of its original features are lost, and it hardly warrants closer inspection.

Pont-ar-Ysgir, 004303 (160)

This charming little bridge is the oldest on Afon Ysgir Fawr and Afon Ysgir Fach, probably dating from the end of the 18th century. Its two semicircular arches span sixteen yards (14.6m) and the bridge is ten feet (3m) wide. There were originally two recesses over the cutwaters, but the downstream one has been partly filled in during repair work. The upstream recess is still in its original form, and the bridge is best viewed from this side, as a crumbling sewer pipe disfigures the downstream face. An unclassified road crosses the bridge and continues along the north side of Afon Wysg to pass over Pont Aberbrân, 984298, and Pont Abercilieni, 938302, both being single arch crossings built during the mid 19th century.

Crickhowell Bridge, 214182 (161)

This fine old stone bridge of thirteen arches spanning one hundred and forty yards (128m) is the longest of its kind in Wales, and also has the highest number of arches. The date of its construction is uncertain, but Jervoise considered it to have been built about the same time as the one at Llangynidr. This is of no great assistance since there is no date for that one either. Around the middle of the 17th century is probably the nearest that one can accept, as it was recorded at the sessions of 1690 as being 'Ancient'. Although there was a bridge here as early as 1538, it was unlikely to be of stone.

A contract was drawn up in April 1706 in which William Powell of Llangattock was to be paid four hundred pounds in two instalments to build the bridge, and maintain it for a further eleven years. By 1735 more repairs were needed, and this time three masons were contracted to keep the bridge in repair for eleven years.

Early in the 19th century it was considered to be 'unalterably bad and should be entirely rebuilt'. The writer, (Theophilus Jones) goes on to say that:

> 'it is at present so narrow it would be vain for two carriages of any description to attempt to cross at the same time.

Nothing appears to have been done and around 1915 Rees remarked that the:

> long and narrow bridge at Crickhowell rendered romantic by its dilapidation cannot but inspire the passenger with fear.

Repairs did eventually happen in 1930 when the bridge was widened, on the upstream side, to eighteen feet (5.4m). The town end was rebuilt at the same time, reducing the number of arches from fourteen to thirteen. Observers might note that there is a discrepancy between the upstream and downstream views, because only twelve arches can be counted from one side! The holes that can be seen under the arches were used to hold the scaffolding. A stone seat still survives in one downstream recess, but it is no longer needed as pavements have been built on both sides. The bridge is by no means attractive with its hotchpotch of low, different sized arches, but it is interesting and has a good supply of viewing points.

Llangynidr Bridge, 153203 (161)

Jervoise considered this to be 'one of the most interesting bridges over the Usk'. The date of building is not recorded but the sessions record that it was repaired around 1707. In 1700 William Powell the Llangattog bridge-builder was entrusted with the sum of three hundred and fifty pounds to build a 'bridge of stone with pillars of stone in the water'. We do not know how long the work took to complete, but it must have been finished by 1706 when he began work on the bridge at Crickhowell.

The bridge built by William Powell is most probably the one there today, but he does not appear to have been particularly workmanlike in his approach for only sixteen years later more repairs were needed. The repair contract of nine pound ten shillings bound Anthony Prees to 'repair the said bridge of all defects as well as in the water and above the water and to cover the walls thereof on either side with Mortar and Lime and to make a pitching or paving and to lay a good frame of firm wood to be fastened with iron pins'. If that wasn't enough he was expected to keep the bridge in good repair for a further five years.

It has escaped any widening, which makes it all the more interesting, but at only nine feet (2.7m) wide, and on a busy road, it creates problems for vans and lorries. Its six segmental arches span eighty yards (73.5m) and the recesses over the cutwaters are as much in demand today as when they were built.

Private land prevents viewing from the northern side, but access to the downstream side at the town end is not difficult. This attractive and well preserved bridge is well worth a detour from the A40 at Bwlch, but you will find signs that remind you of the narrow width, so do not be tempted into taking your caravan.

Glangrwyney Bridge *(Pont Llangrwyne)*, 238163 (161)

Upriver from Abergavenny, Afon Wysg is joined by a number of rivers that are crossed by some interesting but less important bridges. Pont Llancrwyne *(Glancrwyney Bridge)*, built by Andrew Maud of Brecon in 1773, has three arches one of which is over a road to a private house. The original downstream side has a recess and a massive cutwater and this side is well worth viewing. It has been widened and recently repointed on the upstream side, and a metal footway installed.

Pont Llangenni, 241179 (161)

Pont Llangenni, a little further upriver, has a single segmental arch with two openings in the haunches, one of which has been partially filled in during road improvements. The bridge is only ten feet (3m) wide, with sharp bends at each approach.

Above Llangenni on Afon Grwyne Fach a number of small bridges can be seen. Some of these are of great age, but the one at Bont has been ruined by the insertion of a concrete roadway over the arch.

Pont Felindre, 179232 (161)

Afon Rhiangoll is a beautiful name for a small river, and the bridge that straddles it at Felindre is well worthy of it. The water cascades over a weir near the bridge, and there are attractive houses nearby. It is altogether a truly idyllic scene.

Jervoise, who did not find much to impress him on this river, describes the bridge as 'the only remarkable one', and it has weathered a little more during the years since he visited it.

He made no suggestions as to its age, which could be any time from the beginning to the middle of the 19th century, but it has remained unaltered since. It is so small and delicate as to be more of a model than the real thing. Its two segmental arches span only twelve yards (11m), and the bridge is only seven feet (2.1m) wide. It also has small recesses.

Devil's Bridge, Clydach Gorge, 238141 (161)

The original bridge was built in the late 1700s, and according to the Brecknockshire Sessions was rebuilt and widened from eight feet (2.4m) to twelve feet (3.6m) in 1826. A single elliptical arch over the gorge, it takes its name from the supposed image of the devil in the rocks below.

Pen-y-bont, Llanfihangel Crucornau, 325209 (161)

This bridge isn't of great interest, but passers by may wish to read the inscription on the plaque that was removed from an earlier bridge when it was rebuilt and the parapet increased in height. It states:

> This bridge was built at the expense of the County in the sixth year of the reign of George the fourth in the year of our Lord 1827 by Mathew William Skenfrith and William Coney Monmouth.

The downstream side is covered in virginia creeper, making an attractive splash of colour in autumn.

Pont Rhys Powel, 322221 (161)

This neat little bridge on the road to Cwmyoy is built of red sandstone. It isn't of great age, but it is well maintained, the two arches and cutwaters having been repointed recently.

Pont yr Esgob, 285212 (161)

The present single arched bridge appears to be fairly recent, although the bridge is only nine feet (2.7m) wide. The abutments are from an earlier construction. On the road from Cwmyoy to the church at Partrishaw, it no doubt derived its name (The Bishops bridge) from its user or builder.

The name has been corrupted to 'Pont Ysgib', and appears as such on the larger scale maps.

Pont Pantysgallog, 905293 (160)

Little is known about this bridge which is named after the nearby farm, 'the hollow of the thistle'. It was also known as Pont y Gof, *(blacksmiths bridge)* and Pont y Rhyd, *(ford bridge)* and there is a fine illustration of it by J.G. Wood, in his 'Principal Rivers of Wales' (1813).

This lofty semicircular arch is considered by many to be the finest single arched bridge in the old County of Brecknockshire. It span is sixteen yards (14.6m) and the road narrows to only eight feet (2.4m) at the top. It is very much the type of bridge one finds depicted on Christmas cards and 19th century prints, stirring the imagination to expect a coach and four to come rattling down the steep hill on either side.

The road from the A40 leads over Pont Pantysgallog to Crai, and if you are brave enough to drive along it, the second turning on the right will bring you to 'Pont Nant-yr-Haern (895265). Built by Thomos Price in 1844, the plaque is too badly worn to reveal much of this fact.

For those who wish to confine their visit to Pont Pantysgallog, it is probably easier to park on the A40 and walk the short distance to the bridge. You may be tempted to cross over the wooden fence to view the bridge from the river bank, but the land owners are not happy about this.

The bridge was built during the late 1770s, and there is little indication of any great rebuilding, apart from regular repointing which has kept it in fine condition. It is a bridge that should not be missed.

Pantysgallog is the last (or first) bridge of any importance on Afon Wysg. The next one upriver, Pont Newydd was according to the Quarter Sessions of 1681, 'ruinated and carried away by flood', and its successors must have suffered much the same fate, as the present crossing is built of iron girders.

Pontarhydfer 862275 (160)

The bridge was built by Evan Hargest of Brecon who contracted the work in August 1855, and was given one month to complete the work. He was to be paid one hundred and fifty-seven pounds to build a bridge 'in a proper workmanlike and substantial manner of the best materials', and maintain it for a period of seven years.

It had been proved prior to setting out the contract that oak piles were required as foundations, which had to be around five inches

131

(12.7cm) in diameter and eight feet (2.4m) in length tipped with iron sockets and driven in six inches (15.2cm) apart. It was not an easy contract for the builder, who had to pay two assistants out of the money allocated, as well as a road over the bridge and a hundred yards on either side. The contract insisted on high quality work and gives details of methods of dressing required on the stones.

The builder must have also been hard pushed to complete the bridge within the time given, and we will never know if he made a profit on the venture.

Jervoise describes this bridge as 'a single stone arch of rusticated masonary', and it still stands today, despite the constant battering of heavy traffic.

Jervoise described this bridge as 'a single stone arch of rusticated masonry', a well used phrase of his when no information was available for an accurate dating.

Old Pontarsenni was replaced some years ago by a modern structure, but a little downriver at 933262 an interesting single arch which is partly covered in vegation, connects a farm with the road. Its cobbled roadway gives it an older appearance than it really is.

The only suspension bridge over the upper reaches of Afon Wysg is the private crossing between Abersefin and Abercamlais bridges. It is not accessible and cannot be seen from the road, but it is reputed to be an interesting 19th century construction.

Pont Blaen-cwm Du, 943214 (160)

This small bridge is insignificant in appearance, and is usually ignored by the hardy walkers of the grassed track between Fforest-lodge and Maen Llia. Much of the track formed the Roman Road of Sarn Helen, but a proper road was built by the Turnpike Trust in the mid-18th century to link the top of Cwm Nedd (the Neath Valley) with the Aberhonddu/ Brecon road. There is reason to believe that this little bridge dates from that time. It ranks with less than half a dozen others as being among the most remote in Wales, and only the dedicated walker will consider it worth the effort to go and view it.

Tredunnock Bridge, 385948 (171)

Travellers turning sharp right after crossing Afon Llwyd east of Caerleon, on the way to Tredunnock, will no longer find an ivy covered structure at a point on the map named Ivybridge. The high, single arch bridge over a small stream has been bricked up and culverted. There are no bridges of interest over Afon Llwyd either, since the one mentioned earlier was rebuilt and widened in 1836. Jervoise names it Pont-y-Goron, but the original name was Pont Sadwrn, *(Saturday Bridge)* and one wonders at the reason for such an unusual name.

The bridge at Tredunnock over Afon Wysg is a particularly fine structure with stepped buttressed cutwaters, each step surmounted by an overhanging course and terminating in recesses. Its three segmental arches are best seen from downstream. The length is fifty-seven yards (52m) and it is thirteen feet (3.9m) wide. There is no plaque, but it is generally accepted that it was built by David Edwards during the early 1780s. It is in fine condition although the road engineers have seen fit to pin part of the structure in recent years, which will hopefully preserve it from future damage. The small hamlet that developed east of the bridge is, much as expected, named Newbridge on Usk.

Usk Bridge, 374007 (171)

There was a bridge at Usk *(Brynbuga)* in the 14th century and Nigel Chepstow, the great benefactor of river crossings in the area, left money in his will to repair this as well as others. The first stone structure is reputed to have been built by William Edwards around 1760, his second contract after his final success at Pontypridd. The bridge was widened by some three feet (90cm) on either side in 1836, and the original structure can still be detected forming the core of the present bridge. At the same time the approaches were filled to make the gradients easier. At ninety yards (82cm) long and twenty-seven feet (8.2m) wide its five arches, even with recent flood prevention work to compete with, still present an attractive sight when viewed from the only suitable position, which is downstream on the western side. Much of the bridge is built of red sandstone, and a plaque inserted into the parapet in now completely devoid of any inscription.

Chain Bridge, 346055 (171)

A bridge of oak was built at this point in 1730 to replace an earlier weaker structure that was washed away in a flood. It was eventually to be replaced again in 1829 by the original chain bridge constructed by Brown Lenox of Pontypridd. So named because it was supported by huge chains, the name was adopted by the present iron bride when it was reconstructed in 1906. A bronze plaque records the event, and goes on to list all the dignitaries involved and their numerous qualifications to such an extent that the actual builder, George Palmer of Neath, could only have his name squeezed in at the end by having it shortened to Geo.

The bridge, which is showing signs of deterioration, can only be viewed from the roadway, and is a typical example of bowed girder construction.

Pont Pantygoetre, 348089 (161)

An imposing stone bridge of three elliptical arches built about 1821, the same time as the one further upriver at Llanelen with the same attractive rounded pillars at the end of the haunches. Its most unique features are the circular openings, one in each of the haunches, and a further pair in the two piers. It is one of only a few bridges where openings in the piers are used as a decorative feature as well as to lighten the construction, the other being at Cenarth on Afon Teifi.

The bridge is eighteen feet wide and because this stretch of straight road encourages some fast moving traffic, care is required as there is no footway. There is a good view from both up and downstream on the western side where the Usk Valley Path follows the bank. The builder was John Upton of Gloucester.

Llanelen Bridge, 305110 (161)

Two miles south of Abergavenny the A4042 crosses Afon Wysg at Llanelen over a large, impressive structure of three segmental arches. The centre arch being higher and wider than those on either side gives the bridge an elegant appearance from the river bank. The land owners of the northern end of the bridge make it known in no uncertain terms that you cannot view from their side, but there is access down a steep and often muddy path to the downstream bank on the other side. Sewer pipes run across both faces of the bridge, ruining its appearance. The plaque on the downstream parapet states that it was, *designed and builded by John Upton of Gloucester, Engineer, 1821, for the County of Monmouth.*

Usk Bridge Abergavenny *(Y Fenni)*, 292139 (161)

According to the Rev. J. Evans in his *Topographical and Historical Description of the County of Monmouth* published in 1809, this was 'a fine old bridge of thirteen arches'. The number have now been reduced to seven over the river, and a further three in the approaches which are almost completely silted up. Of the seven arches, four are pointed and three are segmental, which indicates a great deal of rebuilding during its lifetime. There is no information as to the time the stone arches were first built, but the pointed ones would suggest a sixteenth century construction.

The span is now seventy yards (64m), and the original width of twelve feet (3.6m) has been extended on the upstream side to twenty-seven (8.2m). A major flood prevention scheme has reshaped the banks, and the arch nearest the town has been recently rebuilt, but does not distract from the original structure.

Gastineau's illustration of 1830 includes a much higher stone viaduct which presumably carried a tramway, and in the photograph taken by Jervoise, an iron railway bridge had taken its place. This has now been removed leaving an uncluttered view from the downstream bank.

129210 (161)
This is an attractive suspension bridge that was built in 1925 for pedestrians. It now carries a water main.

Bridges of Gwent

The Monnow Bridge, 505125 (162)

This bridge, just inside the Welsh border at Monmouth, has had difficulties in maintaining its connections with Wales and is often upstaged by better known, but far less historically important, bridges further west. It is in fact quite unique, being the only remaining bridge in the British Isles that still has its original fortified tower as part of the structure.

There is an interesting publication which deals in detail with its history.

Unconfirmed sources state that it was built around 1617, and widened in 1879. It has three semicircular arches spanning around forty yards (37m), and the present width between the parapets is about twenty-four feet (7.3m). According to Jervoise it has been widened by around four feet (1.2m) on the upstream side and five feet (1.5m) on the downstream, these additions being added to the sides of three wide ribs built into the arches.

The tower, which is situated over the town end piers, consists of an archway ten feet (3m) wide, and two small openings in the sides, now used by pedestrians. The pavement has in fact taken up most of the widening.

There was a bridge here in the 13th century, presumably of a wooden construction as traces of timber piers were recently discovered during flood prevention works. Bridges in this area were the property of the Duke of Beaufort but little information is available from that source as the family archives were destroyed at Raglan Castle in the 17th century.

It was ignored by most of the early travellers, possibly because it was not on any recognised tourist route. It is not easy to obtain a good view of the bridge, but its historical importance is such that it should not be ignored despite its location on the very border of Wales.

Pont-y-meistr, 246895 (171)

Jervoise considered this to be the most interesting bridge on Afon Ebbw, and at the time of my survey still existed, surrounded by trunk roads and concrete flyovers.

History does not record the name of the 'Master' who built it, but there is a local tradition that he built the bridge in order to impress a lady friend by driving over it in a coach to pay her a visit. The bridge is a fine construction of two arches and massive cutwaters with rounded stone

136

parapets. It is nine feet (2.7m) wide and twenty-four yards (22m) long, and has survived the years with little sign of wear and tear.

Gwent River Bridges

Aber-big *(Aberbeeg)* Packhorse Bridge, 210020 (171)

There are very few stone river bridges in the valleys of Gwent that are old enough to be considered ancient. Most were ravaged when, in the words of Alexander Cordell, this fair country was raped for iron and coal. One of the few to survive was the single arch over Afon Ebbw Fach at Aber-big. It was 'found' and briefly noted by Jervoise who, judging from his lack of comments, did not consider it of much importance. It was rediscovered by Fred Hando the Gwent artist and historian, who sketched it complete with iron railings, and recorded that it was surrounded by modern 'clutter'.

The railings have since been replaced by a brick parapet, and bearing in mind the redevelopment around it, its survival is remarkable. Although it is referred to as a packhorse bridge, its width of nine feet (2.7m) is wider than average for that type of bridge, and there is little doubt that it was also used by wheeled vehicles. Attempts at dating it can only be speculative, with mid to late-18th century being the most likely time of its construction.

Bigsweir Bridge, 538052 (161)

A beautiful single arch iron bridge over Afon Gwy *(Wye)* just above Tintern. The design has often been attributed to Telford, but it is probably the work of George Hollies who designed similar bridges in the Border Counties. The span is one hundred and sixty feet (49m).

265136 (161)

This is a small stone bridge in the middle of Gofilon, with a single arch of thin stone slabs. It may not be as old as it appears, and there are possibly many similar bridges tucked away in narrow streets in rural villages, but it is well worth an inspection.

512128 (162) Wye Bridge, Monmouth

The bridge of five semicircular arches in red sandstone was built early in the 17th century. R. Waugh in his *Guide to Monmouth* (1878) states that on the third pier 'the date 1617 is seen faintly on a shield'. There was a gateway on the bridge, but this was removed at the beginning of the 19th century.

The bridge was widened on both sides in 1879 giving a total width of thirty feet (9.1m), and the present bridge is of that date. The total span is seventy-eight yards (71m). It is marked as an antiquity on the latest series of OS Leisure Maps.

Rhymni Valley Bridges

The only remaining stone road bridges in this industrialised valley are those between Caerffili and Llanedeyrn, where the land has remained largely pastoral. All were visited by Jervoise and have remained in much the same condition, carrying unclassified roads.

Pont Bedwas, 170884 (171)

This bridge is reputed to have been built by David Edwards around 1790. It has been subjected to a great deal of patchwork repairs, and yet retains much of its character. Something similar to a milestone has been inserted into the upstream parapet but the inscription is quite illegible apart from *18 0*. The most important figure has been chipped away. The stone was probably installed during repair work. The parapets are much higher than one would expect on a bridge of that period, and were no doubt rebuilt as were the double stepped cutwaters which now come up to the top of the parapets.

There are two arches spanning twenty-two yards (20m) and the roadway is thirteen feet (3.9m) wide. As one would expect, it is subjected to a weight restriction and the downstream side is once again obscured by a sewer pipe, although this one is not fixed to the stonework.

Pontydraethen, 224876 (171)

This bridge has suffered more than the others, although it was probably built only a little earlier and could be the same one shown on Cary's map of 1787.

It has two arches but its twenty-three yard (21m) length does not include the further two land arches. At only nine feet (2.7m) wide it is not surprising that its low parapets, under two feet (60cm) high, have been completely demolished and replaced by a wire fence. The recesses however have been rebuilt, possibly because they are still needed. The remainder of the bridge also shows signs of haphazardous repair, but enough of the original remains to make it worthy of interest.

Michaelston Bridge, 231845 (171)

This bridge is in much better condition having been well maintained and strengthened around the piers with concrete. It has not been rebuilt to any great extent, and most of the stonework appears to be from the original construction of around 1780. There are just two arches, a roadway of just ten feet (3m) and recesses over the cutwaters. The string course on the upstream side is probably part of the original construction.

Pont Cefn Llwyd, 231834 (171)

Sometime known as 'Kevenmably Bridge' it has been subjected to some considerable rebuilding, particularly on the downstream side. There are two arches and recesses, and a roadway of ten feet (3m) width.

Chepstow Bridge, 533944 (162)

The bridge over the Wye at Chepstow that was mentioned by William of Worcester in 1478 was probably a wooden structure, but there is speculation among local historians that wooden stakes discovered in the mud nearby some years ago might have been of Roman origin. By the time Leyland arrived the bridge was in 'need of repair', which resulted in John Falkner, Alderman of Gloucester making a bequest of forty pounds in his will to build a new 'goodly bridge of timber', stipulating that it had to be completed within a year of his death. This took place in 1545, and in 1587 the counties of Monmouth and Gloucester became responsible for its repair. Joint ownership of bridges always caused problems, and Chepstow Bridge was no exception. An engraving by Buck in 1732 shows a timber bridge supported by a stone pier in the middle, but an engraving by Colt Hoare from the last decade of the 18th century depicts a house built in the middle with stone piers on the one side and wooden supports on the other. This suggests that the two counties could not agree on the type of bridge to be built. Several theories have been put forward regarding the use of the building in the centre, including the suggestion that it was a frontier post between Wales and England. The existing bridge is a superb example of the use of cast iron lattice girder construction, and consists of five arches resting on stone piers. The designer and builder was John Rennie, and it is one hundred and thirty-two yards (121m) long but only twenty feet (6.1m) wide.

A new bypass bridge some distance downstream, which also provides a good viewing point, has relieved the old bridge of having to carry heavy through traffic, but passage across it is still controlled by lights. It has recently been painted and is in excellent condition.

On both sides of the iron railings in the middle are cast iron letters which state that it was built in Anno Domini 1816, and on either side *Monmouth* and *Gloucester* marks the boundary line.

Troy Viaduct, 514121 (162)

This is an impressive but crumbling stone viaduct spanning Afon Gwy *(Wye)* below Monmouth, and named after the nearest railway station. Built around 1860 as part of the Wye valley rail network, it saw almost a hundred years of service before falling victim to that sweeping curtailment of rural lines, known as the 'Beeching Plan'.

The height is low by normal viaduct standards; a mere forty feet (12.2m). The twenty arches span three hundred feet (91m), and although little known outside the area, it is well worth recording.

Early Glamorganshire Iron Bridges

Only a few of the early cast iron bridges erected during the birth of the iron making foundries of Glamorgan and Gwent survive, (see Demolished bridges). The less than half a dozen that remain are under constant threat from rust, the elements, and cash starved local authorities who are unable to meet the cost of maintaining them. One has been partly rebuilt as part of a heritage scheme at Chapel Row in Merthyr, but another is still rusting in the corner of Cyfarthfa Park.

Pontycafnau, 37071 (160)
In early 1793 William Crawshaw, the Merthyr ironmaster, started to build a tramroad from the Gurnos Limestone Quarries to his works at Cyfarthfa. The work was under the supervision of his engineer, Watkin George, a man of some consideration ability, and the project included an iron bridge over the Taf gorge opposite Cyfarthfa Castle.

The bridge was of cast iron and was constructed in an A form with raking struts. It combined an aqueduct and tramway. The present structure is all that remains of a large two tier iron aqueduct erected to supply water to power a large water wheel at the works, and to replenish the Glamorgan Canal which was often short of water.

Little of the original aqueduct remains, but a sketch and engraving by Penry Williams gives some idea of its impressive size. In 1802 Walter Davies (Gwallter Mechain) described the structure during his tour of Glamorgan as being 'eighty feet above the bed of the river at low water and extends about six hundred feet in length'.

The surviving structure of Pontycafnau has two bolt holes at the top of the centre support which fitted into one of the upper aqueduct braces. This bridge is among the first iron tramway crossings and aqueducts to be built. A second bridge was cast in the same pattern and stood at the head of the canal, but none of it has survived.

Pontycafnau is now some fifteen yards (13.7m) long and a little under six feet (1.8m) wide. It has remained unchanged, but the iron struts are badly rusted and need some form of protection if this bridge is to survive.

It can be seen by turning down the road that leads to a small industrial estate opposite the lake at Cyfarthfa Castle Park. A short walk through the many gaps in the fence will lead you to the bridge, which is safe enough to cross.

003035 (170)

This cast iron bridge at Robertstown in Aberdâr was built in 1811 to carry a tramroad across Afon Cynon. The bridge is supported on four cast iron arched ribs. One of its most interesting features is the ridged metal roadway along the centre, which prevented the horses that were hauling the trams from slipping.

The bridge is nine feet (2.7m) wide and eleven yards (10m) long and both the iron sections and the stone abutments have recently been restored. The easiest access is from the west bound carriageway of the Aberdâr bypass, and there is a convenient layby near the bridge.

854917 (170)

This is a small footbridge of cast iron situated at the top of the car park in Maesteg. The date of construction is unknown, but it was cast at the nearby iron works. The bridge now carries a concrete roadway, and the iron railings are a much later addition.

Smarts Bridge 232128 (161)

This attractive cast iron bridge spanning Afon Clydach was built in 1824. The Clydach iron works were established in 1789 and their remains can still be seen, although much of it was destroyed during the building of the 'Heads of the Valleys' road in 1964. Smarts Bridge is one of the finest of the early iron bridges remaining in Glamorgan and Gwent. The main structure consists of iron lattice girders, with the roadway assembled from three cast panels, grooved to take carriage wheels. It was also fitted with protruding lumps to prevent slipping, similar to another bridge at Aberdâr.

The bridge was restored in 1987 and treated with a rust inhibitor which should ensure its survival for a while, and new railings were added as a safety precaution. Only nine feet (2.7m) above the river bed, the authorities still considered them necessary, but the heavy stone walls they built to secure them are distracting and out of character.

Old Pont-ar-Daf during 1989 drought

Builth Wells Bridge – old print by W. Radclyffe

Boroughrood Bridge

Caersws Bridge

146

Long Bridge, Newton

Llandinam Bridge

Pont Corwen

Pont Carrog

Pont Llangollen

Chain Bridge, Llangollen

Haverfordwest Old Bridge

Pont Hywel

Plaque on Llandeilo bridge   *Pont Llaeron*

Pont Dolauhirion

Pont Gogoian

Pont Aberteifi

Pontnewydd ar Aeron

Pont Trefechan – Rowlandson drawings, 1797

The new Britannia Bridge

Pont y Borth

154

Conwy Suspension Bridge

Pont-sarn-ddu

155

Miners Bridge (Pontymwynwyr)

Waterloo Bridge (Y Bont Haearn)

Y Bont Fawr, Llanrwst

Pont-y-pair
old print by S. Middiman

Penmaenpool Toll Bridge

Pont Sgethin

Pont Minllyn

Pont Glan Gwynedd

Pant y Goetre Bridge,
Gwent

Clapper Bridge,
Castle Upon Alun, Glamorgan

River Bridges of Glamorgan *(Morgannwg)*

Bridgend Bridge, 905798 (170)

The original bridge was built in the 16th century, but the present structure is of an 18th century design. Only two arches remain, but the massive cutwaters on the upstream side suggests that there could have been two or three more on either side of the present ones.

The bridge is dwarfed by tall buildings on the town side, which probably accounted for the removal of the other arches. The remaining arches are segmental in shape and the roadway, which is only nine feet (2.7m) between the parapets, is cobbled and still used as a short cut for pedestrians to reach the town centre.

The river at this point was encased within a concrete channel some years ago as part of a massive flood prevention scheme, and the old bridge, like many others that have survived in built up areas, has a rather forlorn and unnatural look about it.

Maesteg Bridges

The town of Maesteg in Dyffryn Llyfni possessed, until recently, a number of bridges that were connected with its industrial past. This number has been reduced in recent years as the inevitable road widening schemes take effect, but for those with the time and inclination to follow Afon Llyfni through the back streets of this small valleys town, a few interesting bridges still survive.

The sole remaining tramway bridge with an elliptical arch and the cast iron bridge in the car park have already been described. The stone 'Parish Bridge' (857911), by Bethel Baptist Chapel, is almost completely covered by council tarmac, but closer examination will reveal that it has been partly rebuilt using rails and sleepers from one of the many disused tramways. The bridge a little downriver has been subjected to much more drastic rebuilding, the top having been removed and the new road supported on concrete pillars that all but obscure the old structure. If you are prepared to endure the close proximity of an unpleasant sewer, it is possible to walk down the river bank and through the two circular flood openings. It was built in 1827 to carry a tramway to connect with the Dyffryn Llyfni and Porthcawl Railway.

Another bridge that was built at the same time over Castle Street was demolished in 1952. The keystone inserted into the wall at the junction of Castle Street and Bridge Street has the inscription, M.I.C. 1827.

Kenson Bridge, 053688 (170)

This is a small bridge which spans the Kenson Stream. It was built around 1870 on what was at that time the main coast road. It has survived without any major improvements but would benefit from a face lift. Jervoise considered it and nearby Burton Bridge as 'fairly modern'. The latter has been sacrificed to the road improvers. Kenson Bridge is eleven feet (10m) wide.

Miskin Bridge *(Pont Meisgyn)* 47808 (170)

The bridge was built to replace a wooden structure called Pont Felin Fawr in the middle of the 16th century. Miskin Bridge has been much improved, with the original width of ten feet (3m) increased to eighteen feet (5.5) on the upstream side. The two pointed arches are eighteen yards (16.4m) long, and there are losenge shaped cutwaters on the downstream side. It is best viewed from this side.

Cymer Concrete Bridge, 856963 (170)

Afon Afan and Afon Corrwg meet at Cymer Afan and have in the past caused severe flooding which destroyed the original stone bridges. A steep and twisting road leads down into the village and up Dyffryn Corrwg. When the new and revolutionary ferroconcrete bridge was built to span the deep ravine in 1936, it was hailed as a breakthrough. Its construction did nothing to ease the traffic problems, which still had to pass through the part of the village that huddles around the river.

At the time of construction it was the longest single span concrete bridge in Wales, and is still an elegant structure, although beginning to show signs of deterioration.

Merthyr Mawr Bridge, 892780 (170)

This is an attractive bridge of three segmental arches and stepped cutwaters, and is typical of the type built by Morgan Thomas. The parapets curve away gracefully to form the approach walls, but at only eleven feet (3.3m) wide only one vehicle one pass at a time, and caution is required.

The bridge is in good condition and easily viewed, but it should be noted that the land on both sides is private. It is interesting to note that it was not mentioned by Jervoise, who inspected 'New Inn Bridge' a little upstream.

A sandstone plaque is inserted into the centre of the upstream parapet (see also Inscriptions), which states:

This bridge was finished at the expense of the right honourable Sir John Nichol under the inspection of William Whittington Surveyor. Built by Morgan Thomas of Laleston Mason A.D. 1827.

Morgan Thomas, who built several bridges in the Vale, was born in 1788 and died in 1866, and was buried at Laleston.

New Inn Bridge, 903773 (170)

This fine bridge over Afon Ogwr was built sometime after 1799, as a Yates map of Glamorgan published by Cary in that year did not include a crossing at this point. The bridge is similar to Merthyr Mawr Bridge, and is often referred to as 'The Sheep Dipping Bridge'. This is because of the unique thirty inch square (76cm^2) openings in the parapets. The two openings, both on the downstream side, were intended to allow the sheep to be propelled into the pool below in order to remove some of the grease and dirt from the fleece before shearing. This is the only bridge of which I am aware with such a feature.

There are four pointed arches, and the total span is twenty-eight yards (25.6m). At only eight feet (2.4) wide, it is one of the narrowest bridges still in use in Glamorgan. The bridge has recently been repointed and is in good condition and well worth a visit.

Leckwith Bridge, 158752 (171)

Apart from the rebuilding of the centre arch, this bridge has remained almost unchanged since it was recorded by Leyland, and is the only surviving bridge that he mentioned over Afon Elái (Ely). Leckwith bridge, on the outskirts of Cardiff, is surrounded by concrete flyovers and new roads, and is under threat because it is still used as the only access to a concrete products site. Apart from the installation of concrete posts in some of the recesses, little has been done to safeguard the bridge.

The bridge was bypassed in 1935 by a typical thirties ferroconcrete construction. When the foundations were being excavated blackened wood piles of great age, from an earlier bridge, were unearthed. Jervoise had inspected the bridge in 1931 and hoped that every effort would be made to preserve this interesting bridge. The fact that it has escaped demolition is in itself a miracle.

The two arches nearest the banks are pointed, and of a very early period. The rebuilt centre arch is segmental with double arch rings, built in two orders. There are recesses over the cutwaters, and the total span is twenty-six yards (24m) with a width of ten feet (3m).

It can be viewed from the 1935 concrete bridge, which is also worthy of more than a passing glance, but reaching it on foot is a risky venture during periods of heavy traffic.

081927 (170)

This is a small twin arch bridge on the secondary road between Pontypridd and Abercynon, just below the railway viaduct. It is difficult to view due to lavish use of barbed wire, but a sandstone plaque on the downstream parapet gives details of its construction.

This bridge was erected by Surveyors W. Morgan for Glyncynnon, T. Thomos for Hafoddyrnog A.D. 1849. W. Morgan, Contractor.

Rhondda Fawr and Rhondda Fach

Long before industrialisation arrived to ravage these two valleys, they were connected by a number of paths and trackways going back to medieval times. Most of the original bridge sites have remained and retained their original names, but so great and rapid was the development that the first stone bridges to replace the wooden crossings were themselves taken down and rebuilt many times in less than one hundred and fifty years. One such bridge, Pontygwaith, gave its name to the community that grew up around it, (not to be confused by a bridge of the same name over Afon Taf). Downstream, Pont Rheola and Pontycymer (not the one attributed to William Edwards) underwent many changes, the latter being completely rebuilt in 1926.

Pont Lluest Wen above Maerdy is probably the oldest bridge in the Rhondda, and was mentioned in 1770, but the present structure dates from a hundred years later. Its survival is due to its remote position just below the reservoir of the same name at the head of Afon Rhondda Fach. It is an imposing single arch bridge, built of large blocks of Pennant sandstone.

Dyffryn Taf Road Bridges

New Berw Bridge, 077911 (170)
This ferroconcrete bridge was built between 1910 and 1912. It was one of the earliest in South Wales, and has remained in remarkably good condition. It looks particularly imposing when viewed from downstream, but is overshadowed by the railway viaduct higher up.

It takes its name from the original Pont y Berw, an aqueduct built to supply the Glamorgan Canal with water, which was named after Berw Rhondda, the cataract just above. It was a popular spot with Victorian travellers; Gastineau sketched both the aqueduct and the river in 1828, and the Hall's visited it in the late 1850s when the aqueduct was leaking and in need of repair. They referred to it as the 'Boiling Bridge'. All that remains of the aqueduct are the remains of one pier in the river bed on the eastern side.

Pont Trefforest, 085890 (170)
This three arch bridge between Trefforest and Glantaf is no longer used by wheeled vehicles, having been blocked at both ends by pavements. The parapets were removed in the 1920s and replaced by two lattice girders supported on steel girders embedded into the roadway. Even this modernisation has been in position long enough not to distract unduly from the piers. The river falls over a weir a little below, and the calm water provides a serene setting.

Taffs Well Bridge, 126825 (171)
There was a crossing here in Leylands time, and Llwyd recorded it as Ynyswern. The present bridge is a massive structure built in Pennant sandstone, and the parapets topped with huge blocks of conglomerate. There are three segmental arches, and cutwaters. It has been bypassed by a concrete bridge for some years, which provides a fine viewing point. The date of construction is uncertain, and although it is of the same type as the demolished Pont Llandaf lower down, it was probably built some years later.

Old Bridge, Pontypridd, 074904 (170)
In 1746 the Hundred of Senghennydd contracted William Edwards, a self taught mason, to build a bridge of three arches over Afon Taf in the area now known as Pontypridd. This is a shortened version of 'Pont-y-tŷ-pridd' *(Bridge by the earth house)*, and early illustrations show a building of that type close by. Part of the contract stipulated that the bridge had to

stand for seven years, but it was washed away by floods in about two years and he was obliged to start again. His next attempt was a single stone arch which collapsed twice before he finally succeeded in 1756, (see Failures). The bridge was to become the most famous in Wales, and for the next hundred years drew onlookers from all over the country.

It was not surprising that this bridge was to prove such an attraction. Not only had it been built by an unknown builder at only his third attempt, but it was the longest single span in Britain and probably in Europe. Not all the visitors to the bridge came to admire it. There was a certain amount of sour grapes among the eminent builders of the day who came to find out how an inexperienced builder could have managed such an achievement. There were a great many comments and opinions in the press, and even as late as 1939 experts were carrying out experiments to try to find why this remarkable structure had managed to survive. To engineers, well versed in the theory of arch construction, the sizes are remarkable. Even the ordinary onlooker, with no knowledge of these facts, cannot be anything other than impressed.

The bridge spans one hundred and forty feet (42.5m), part of a one hundred and seventy-five foot (53.3m) diameter circle. It is thirty-five feet (10.7m) above the bed of the river. The width is almost sixteen feet (4.9m) at the bottom, reducing to just over fourteen feet (4.3m) at the top, and the roadway is only eleven feet (3.3m) wide at the top of the arch. There are three cylindrical openings in each spandrel, reducing in diameter, and the arch stones are only thirty inches (76cm) in width.

The success of the construction was entirely due to the circular openings which reduced the weight on the haunches, (see Construction Techniques), but it is interesting to note that although William Edwards went on to build a further nine, and possibly eleven, bridges, this was to remain his longest arch.

The bridge has undergone some repairs, but the basic structure remains unaltered. The roadway was raised in 1826 to make crossing easier. A stone inserted into the side wall records an earlier repair:

William Edwards 1750, repaired by Edward David and Thomas Evans 1798.

The roadway is at present in the form of steps, these having been placed there in the 1930s. It ceased to carry wheeled traffic in 1856 when the new iron bridge was built alongside. There was a considerable outcry among those who subsequently came to view the new marvel, which ruined once and for all the chance to admire the full sweep of the arch without obstruction. My object in researching bridges is to create an awareness that will lead to their preservation, but if there is one I would like to see demolished, it is this metal monstrosity that has for so long ruined the appearance of this remarkable bridge at Pontypridd. The bridge and the chapel nearby are now part of a heritage centre, and its future is hopefully safe thanks to the sympathy and interest shown by the local authority. A biography of William Edwards, which includes details of building the bridge and the aftermath, by H.P. Richards is well worth reading.

Pont-y-gwaith, 080976 (170)

This bridge should not be confused with a small town of the same name in the Rhondda Fach. It is one of the finest old bridges on Afon Taf, a tall single arch similar to the one at Pontypridd. The date of construction is uncertain, but a wooden bridge was recorded here in 1828, and it is thought that the present structure was built shortly afterwards. The area is one of the oldest iron furnace sites in Merthyr. A cast iron bar was discovered here in 1815 with the date 1478 stamped into it. Another piece with the figures '1555 E.K.' marked on it was also considered to have been cast in the area.

The bridge is not easy to find. Turn down a narrow lane off the A470 between Edwardsville and Mount Pleasant. There is a cattle grid and a farm gate across the approach to the bridge, and a rough farm track on the other side.

This fine old bridge deteriorated badly during the 1980s and was closed in 1989. It has since been restored and is now a grade 2 listed structure.

The road from the A470 down to Pont-y-gwaith passes over a high elliptical arch over a section of the original Taff Vale Railway track. It probably dates from the 1830s, and although a large part of it is now covered in ivy, what is visible is a solid dry stone bridge of some interest.

607965 (170)

This is a stone bridge of two arches over Afon Taf at Quakers Yard. It is covered in ivy and disfigured by large sewer pipes across both faces. It somehow lacks character, the concrete flood prevention wall and road widening not helping. A badly worn plaque on the upstream parapet provides the very basic information:

H.T.   B.H.   1881, T.E. Harvey   C.E.

Afon Taf Fawr and Taf Fechan rise on the southern slopes of the Brecon Beacons, and have filled a number of reservoirs before they join at Merthyr and become Afon Taf. It is a turbulent river and even in the last two decades has been the cause of severe flooding in the City of Cardiff. In the middle of the 16th century there were only four bridges over Afon Taf, all built of wood. The reason given by Leyland was that:

the water of Taphe cummith so doun from woody hilles and often bringgith down such logges and trees that the cuntery wer not able to make up the bridges if they were of stone they should so often be broken.

No stone bridges survive below Taffs Well; the fine three arch bridge of sandstone at Llandaf, after much mauling, was finally removed some years ago when a new crossing was built. Old Cardiff Bridge, built by James Parry of Hay in the 1790s had to make way for the new bridge in 1931, and the Clarence Road lattice girder bridge was removed without a word of protest.

Pontsarn (Bridge), 045098 (160)

This small bridge of a single arch spans Afon Taf Fechan a little downstream of the Railway Viaduct. It lies on the route of the Roman Road over to Brecon, but although rustic in appearance was not built until after 1848, when T.E. Clarke in his *Guide to Merthyr Tydfil* describes the crossing as: 'the bridge is a wooden structure nine feet in width. It was formerly much narrower and consisted of only a few planks'. Theophilus Jones in his *History of Breckonshire* recorded 'a tremendous wooden bridge called Pontsarn thrown from rock to rock'. This was around 1809. The bridge crosses a wild and rugged ravine, this being its greatest feature.

Pont-cefn, Cefncoed Bridge, 029078 (160)

This is a small bridge of a single elliptical arch rebuilt around 1804, on the upstream side of the concrete structure. It is not used by vehicles, but is thirteen feet (14m) wide and covered in ivy. It is worth an inspection. There is a pleasant, if muddy, walk along the path below.

The A470 between Cefncoedycymer and Storey Arms has been improved and straightened a number of times. This has resulted in a number of stone bridges over the many streams that feed and reservoirs from the east being bypassed. Most are not of a great age, probably dating from the mid-19th century. The best preserved is Pont Nant-wern Ddu. It can be found next to the parking area between the Llwyn Onn and Cantref reservoirs. The two large iron pipes on both sides ruin what would otherwise be a picturesque stone bridge.

169

Castle Upon Alun Clapper Bridge, 910752 (170)

This unique little bridge, which is not well known, is situated alongside the narrow road between Castle Upon Alun and Wallas Fach. It is one of the very few clapper type bridges to have survived in Wales, and although there is not an accurate record of its age, it could be from as early as the beginning of the 10th century.

It straddles Afon Alun, which is little more than a stream, although at this point it is wide and shallow. It spans some thirty-five yards (32m) with an overall width of just under six feet (1.8m), and a height of about five feet (1.5m). There are four openings in all; three on the western side and the other at the eastern end. Two of the western openings are original and consist of large slabs of limestone laid over square openings, each some three feet (90cm) wide. The next has the appearance of a later construction in a crude shallow arch while the eastern opening has recently been badly repaired in concrete, over an earlier effort of stone blocks supported on a rusting iron bar.

The local authorities now include the bridge in its leaflet on places of interest, but it is regrettable that it cannot carry out some badly needed minor repairs. This is a fascinating little bridge with many interesting features notably the rough two tier cutwaters of massive stone slabs. A short distance away the road passes under a lofty railway bridge, with a superb skew arch of blue bricks, and further on crosses the river through a ford, alongside which is a series of stepping stones that are probably as old as the bridge.

Although it is possible to drive to the bridge, the road is not for the faint hearted or the owners of large vehicles. It can however be included in a walk from either Castle Upon Alun or the Ewenni to Tregolwyn (*Colwinston*) road. The surrounding woodland is famous for its spring display of wild daffodils, and the disused quarries nearby have been known to yield some interesting fossils.

Pont Castell-nedd *(Bridge)*, 750978 (170)

Afon Nedd was crossed at, or near, the present site as early as 1307 when, in a charter to the Abbey of Nedd, mention was made of 'lands by the bridge'. Leyland in 1538 recorded that the river was spanned by a 'bridge of timbre', and in 1678 the 'paved causeway of Neth bridge was out of repair'. A traveller during the late 18th century described the bridge at the time as 'a structure of one part wood and the other of stone'. In 1792 the South Wales Association for the improvements of roads pointed out that: 'Neath bridge is out of repair and in a dangerous condition'. The report went on to express the damage that the insecure structure would cause to the mail route, and subscriptions were invited to pay for a new bridge.

The last record of subscriptions was in 1800 and it is probable (although there is no written record to confirm this) that the present bridge was completed at around this time. It consists of three segmental arches over the river, and a smaller one over the canal. As this section of the Tennant canal was under construction at around the same time, it seems likely that the builders were able to incorporate the two crossings into one structure.

By the time Jervoise arrived to carry out his survey in 1931 the width of twenty-two feet (6.7m) had been considered too narrow to include a pavement, and the footways had been installed as iron brackets resting on the cutwaters, a common and effective practice seen on many similar bridges.

The life of the bridge as a carrier of wheeled vehicles came to an abrupt halt in the 1970s when the building of a bypass to the town went through the western abutment, between the canal and the railway line. This fine bridge was later subjected to further deformity by having another pedestrian footway installed into its roadway to provide a crossing over the bypass.

Bridges of the Upper Afon Gwy *(Wye)*

Afon Gwy, like its sister Afon Hafren *(the Severn)* is considered one of the most attractive of Welsh rivers. It soon leaves the country, but unlike the Severn, it returns later on its journey to form part of the boundary between Wales and England. It also rises on the slopes of Pumlumon, only two miles from the source of Afon Hafren, and they flow only a short distance apart for several miles. The floods of 1880 laid waste to all the bridges above Rhaeadr and even the lofty bridge that crossed it there, that had stood firm since it was built by James Parry of Hay towards the end of the 18th century, was dismantled in 1929 and replaced by the present modern crossing.

Builth Wells Bridge, 043512 (147)

This is the first bridge of any importance over Afon Gwy. There had been wooden bridges here from as early as the 13th century, according to Theophilus Jones. Ogilby recorded a 'Wood Bridge', at Builth, and Leyland commented, 'There is noe Bridge on Wye from Hereford to Builth.'

It is an elegant bridge, rising gently towards the centre, and the cutwaters have been faced with iron strips. Jervoise records 'six semicircular arches' but these have now been reduced to four, the two end ones having been incorporated in the flood prevention walls. Colt Hoare confirms the existence of the original number, and describes it as 'a handsome stone bridge of six arches' in 1802.

The remaining arches have recently been lined with concrete, but it is still a 'handsome' structure when viewed from the upstream car park or the river bank, downstream. There are two large recesses above the centre piers and the upstream one displays a huge sandstone plaque on which has been inscribed, at different periods of time, the story of its construction and restoration. The earliest inscription is weathered, but is still readable, and states:

> This bridge was erected at the expense of the counties of Brecon and Radnor by James Parry of Hay ad. 1779. The original after serving its purpose for one hundred years became completely decayed and this stone was put in this place by the inhabitants of Builth A.D. 1879.
>
> The later inscription reads, The Bridge was widened and strengthened by the above counties in 1925, engineers W. Lewis Harpus, O.B.E. Breckonshire T.W. Wishlade A.M.I.C.E. Radnorshire. Contractors Messrs. Hybard, Broadhead, and Co. London.

Broughrood Bridge, 131385 (161)

Broughrood Bridge is a massive stone structure and must rank as one of the best bridges on the upper Gwy. It was built in the 1830s, and the De Winton family of Maesllwch Castle are believed to have sponsored most of the work. In order to appreciate its height and towering elegance it must be viewed from the river bank, from where the four sweeping arches that span the water can be seen to the best effect. The stonework is still in good condition, but some flood damage has eroded one of the cutwaters, and a tree is making a determined effort to grow from a crack just below the parapet. There are also two land arches. The bridge is one hundred and seventy yards (155m) in length.

Crossing the river Wye at this point was normally undertaken by fording, and in 1838 a petition was presented to Parliament to build a bridge at Broughrood ferry. Several good reasons were put forward to strengthen the need for a bridge, ranging from the shortening of the distance to Brecon from twenty-five miles (40km) to fourteen miles (22.5km), making crossing easier in times of flood, particularly for the drovers, and reducing the cost of travelling due to tollgate charges.

The only objection appeared to come from Twm Bach the ferryman who would loose his living from carrying men and cattle across the flooded river when fording was impossible. Like all bridge-building over or near ferry crossings, provisions were made in the Act to buy his ferry, and although this was in effect little more than a compulsory purchase order, it did provide some recompense for loss of earnings. At the time the Boughrood ferry was owned by Walter Wilkins of Maes-llwch who finally agreed to sell it to the Bridge Company for ten shillings.

The usual method ro raise money for bridge-building was by subscriptions, on which interest was paid, and a sum of five thousand pounds was required before work would commence. The contract was entrusted to Evan Wrinston, a local man who had already built up a reputation as a small bridge-builder, and he was given seven years to complete the work. The final cost came to five thousand eight hundred and ninety pounds, which also included the cost of some land for the approaches and some cottages that had to be demolished.

Boughrood bridge was opened in July 1842, but not without considerable difficulties. Parts of the unfinished bridge had been damaged by floods, and extra money had to be allocated for strengthening. The Company also had to threaten the contractor that they would finish the construction themselves when it appeared he would be unable to do so.

A range of tolls were charged to cross the new bridge, and anyone attempting to evade such charges by crossing the river by any other means within six hundred yards (550m) on either side of the bridge was liable to be fined up to a total of five pounds, a considerable amount of money. The payment of a toll to cross Boughrood bridge came to an end as late as 1934.

Pont Marteg, 954714 (147)

This is the single arch bridge, now bypassed, over Afon Marteg just before it joins Afon Gwy between Rhaeadr and Llangurig on the A470. A plaque on the outside of the downstream parapet states that it was 'Built 1884', replacing the earlier stone bridge sketched by many of the passing 18th and 19th century artists.

The bridge is insignificant, and is typical of the small bridges of that period. It can be viewed, at the possible expense of torn clothing, scratched hands, and wet feet, from the point where the two rivers meet below the road.

Llansteffan Suspension Bridge, 114416 (161)

A number of suspension bridges were built over the river below Builth Wells but, with the exception of this one, all have been replaced by modern concrete crossings. A cast metal plaque informs us that it was built by David Rowel and Co, in 1922 and that the original weight limit was five tons, which has now been reduced to two. It is only eight feet (2.4m) wide and this, together with the weight restriction, confines its use to light vehicles only. Although neat enough in appearance it hardly justifies a scramble to the river bank, and this turns out to be something of a disappointment in any case as much of it is hidden by the tall trees on both sides.

It has recently been restored and painted and is a very attractive suspension bridge.

The Wye Tributaries

Pont Gunter, 147335 (161)

Jervoise considered this bridge to be the only one of interest over Afon Llyfni, because of its 'four centered arch of unusual construction'. He also mentioned that it had been widened on the downstream side to fifteen feet (4.6m). It is situated on the narrow road from the A470 to Talgarth, and although it has remained unchanged since he inspected it, there is nothing remarkable about it. Also on the same road is Pont-y-bat, and a plaque reminds those who are inclined to stop that it was reconstructed in 1939.

Pontareithon, 019573 (147)

Afon Ieithon joins Afon Gwy about a mile below Newbridge, and the A470 crosses it half a mile from this point. The thousands of motorists who speed along this stretch of road every year are more often than not totally unaware of this fine bridge as they stamp on their brakes to avoid crashing into its parapets. It is situated on a bend at the bottom of a hill, and there is no safe place to park without obstructing a farm entrance. The river-banks are inaccessible and private and the best way to view it is by asking permission to enter a campsite downstream.

Jervoise considered it to be 'possibly a century old' which suggests that it was built early in the 19th century. It is a fine high bridge of two segmental arches and a circular flood opening low in both haunches. It has recently been repointed and the openings have been wired off to prevent animals wandering through. The wire also collects debris in time of flood.

It is similar in construction to Titley Mill Bridge, three miles north-east of Kington. Titley Mill Bridge was built by the County Surveyor, John Gethin, in 1853 (the date is on the keystone) but there is no record of him building Pontareithon. The bridge is worth seeing however, if only for the flood openings.

River Bridges of Powys

Pontarelan, 904716 (147)

Pontarelan is clearly marked on the O.S. maps and is in one of the most remote places in Wales. Had it not been for the present day driver's insatiable demand for mountain roads on which to travel it would have been left to the mercy of the elements.

A new Bailey type bridge now takes all the traffic, and the old bridge stands forlorn next to a picnic site where you can stretch your legs and read the information on the notice board which tells you all about this wilderness, but alas nothing about the bridge.

There is little doubt that it was rebuilt during the time that the water of Afon Elan were being harnessed to form a reservoir at the turn of the last century. It has a tidy arch and two square flood openings of dressed stone. The battered railings which also date from around this time, indicated that the road was once used by much larger vehicles than it is now.

Ditchyeld Bridge, 279608 (148)

Walkers on the long distance Offa's Dyke Path pay little attention to this bridge, south-west of Presteigne, as they plod over it. It was only when the County indicated that they wanted to remove it that it became knowledge that the bridge was of architectural and historical interest, although the reasons for such a listing are none too clear.

It is a small bridge some seven yards (6,4m) long and ten feet (3m) wide, with a single stone arch and a circular opening on one side serving as a flood opening.

Dyffryn Hafren *(The Severn Valley)* Bridges

The Severn is one of the three fine rivers that rise within a short distance of each other on Pumlumon. It is two hundred and twenty miles (354km) in length and the longest river in Britain, but we will loose interest in it once it has flowed through Offa's Dyke, under Pont Llandrinio, and over the border into Shropshire. There are no bridges of importance above Llanidloes because the river was often fordable and those that have been constructed in recent years are of little interest.

Short Bridge *(Pont Fer)*, Llanidloes 954845 (136)

Two bridges are shown on Saxtons map of 1578 at about the same place as the stone built constructions that are still in use. They have the most unimaginative names (apart from Newbridge) that I have come across, but have inherited them from earlier bridges built of wood. The Quarter Sessions Records report that 'Pont Ferr', over 'the Seavern in the Parish of Llanydloes' was 'out of repair' in 1681, and Long Bridge in 1712.

The present Short Bridge is a solid looking stone arch, sandwiched between the two high walls that control the river in the centre of the town. A plaque on the outside of the downstream parapet, which can be read by those with good eyesight because it is difficult to get close to it, tells us that it was built by *Ths.Penson, County Surveyor, E.D. Jones Builder, formerely of Dolgellau 1849.*

Long Bridge, a short distance downstream, is similar but with three arches and was built in 1826.

Caersws Bridge, 033917 (136)

The next stone bridge on Afon Hafren *(the river Severn)* is the massive structure at Caersws. It was built around 1821, has three elliptical arches, a roadway eighteen feet (5.5m) wide and is sixty yards (56m) long. Its construction was long overdue, the previous wooden bridges being in constant need of repair as the Sessions of 1680 state that 'Ye Bridge of Caresoose, over ye river Suirne' was in disrepair.

Long Bridge, Newtown, 107918 (136)

There was a wooden bridge at Newtown towards the end of the 15th century according to William of Worcester, and one Richard Mathews left forty shillings (two pounds) 'towards repairing the bridge at Newtown' in 1639. Fenton, in 1804, referred to a bridge that was 'old and infirm' but it must have held out for some time afterwards because the present bridge was completed in 1826.

Long Bridge has a pleasant weathered look about it although its three segmental arches are partly obstructed by iron brackets that carry the pavement on both sides. This has increased the overall width to sixteen feet (5m), and the iron arches were installed after an accident on what was previously a very narrow crossing. They were designed by Thomas Penson, who went on to design other iron bridges in the County.

Iron footways running across the face of bridges can often prove disastrous to the general aesthetic appearance, but in the case of Long Bridge they have turned out to be an admirable feature and enhance the character of the bridge.

Llanddewi Bridge, 105683 (136)

Llanddewi Bridge is among the last of the 1930s stone built bridges and has two notable features. There are four recesses with seats, and a long plaque in Welsh. It is unusual to come across Welsh inscriptions on bridges in Anglicized 'Radnorshire', and even more so when they take precedence over the English translation. This one reads:

> *Pont Llanddewi yn Sir Faesyfed. Agorwyd gan Arglwydd Ormathwaite ar y 12 o Orffennaf 1933. Henadur B.P. Lewis Cadeirydd y Cyngor Sirol. Cynghorwr G.R. Davies Cadeirydd Pwyllgor y Ffyrdd.*

Aberbechan Bridge, 144934 (136)

This high, wide and handsome bridge was built to replace a wooden structure in 1855. When viewed from the river bank, its three segmental arches and solid stone construction gives the impression that at last a bridge had been built to defy the regular Severn floods. An unusual feature are the red brick arch rings, which in fact distract from the remainder of the massive stone structure.

Cilcewydd Bridge, 229041 (126)

The present bridge of four segmental arches was built in 1861, the previous wooden crossings being constantly washed away, and large amounts being spent on their repairs. In 1711, for example, two hundred and twenty pounds was spent on 'Kil Kowyth Bridge'.

Buttington Bridge, 246089 (126)

This bridge, the last of the iron arched crossings in Dyffryn Hafren, was designed by W.H. Sweetman in 1872. Although it lacks the intricate iron work of those designed by Thomas Penson, it spans the river in a single sweeping arch of great elegance, and has attractive 'leaf' design railings as parapets.

The present bridge replaced a wooden crossing which had served the site for a great number of years, depending on numerous beneficiaries for repairs. Davyd Elis Preest left twenty shillings to repair 'a certeyne bridge called Bottingtons' when he died in 1548, and a David Lloyd left thirty shillings in 1633.

A bridge was mentioned by Leyland here, and Ogilby's route from Shrewsbury to Welshpool crossed here. In 1682 the Sessions reported that the 'Greate bridge over Sivern called Butintons is out of repair'.

Llandrinio Bridge, 298170 (126)

A bridge was authorised above the ford here in 1769, but not completed until 1775. Pennant called it a 'new and handsome structure'. It was the first stone bridge to be built over Afon Hafren *(the Severn)* in Wales.

There is a touch of the Baroque about it, with its pointed and rusticated voussoirs, and ball finials against pilaster strips. The three semicircular arches span forty-four yards (40m), and it is only twelve feet (3.6m) wide. The date 1775 can be seen on the keystone of the middle arch. It has remained largely unaltered and is one of the most interesting and historically important stone bridges in that area of Wales.

Thomas Penson's Iron Bridges

Thomas Penson was already well established as a bridge builder before he was appointed Montgomeryshire County Surveyor, having successfully built a new bridge at Overton to replace the one which collapsed while under his father's supervision.

He started his appointment in Montgomeryshire modestly enough with a small road bridge over the canal at Aberbechan, but graduated to a wider range of contracts, which included the new church at Newtown and Montgomery jail.

After he had designed and installed the iron brackets to carry the pavements over Long Bridge at Newtown, he felt confident to tackle more ambitious projects, of which the iron bridges at Llandinam and Brynderwen (Aber-miwl) are the best known.

Pont Llandinam, 025886 (136)

Penson was particularly impressed with the work of a local contractor who had started to build small sections of roads, and offered him the chance to build the approach road and abutments to the new iron bridge that he had designed to cross Afon Hafren at Llandinam. The young contractor's name was David Davies who later went on to build railways and open coalmines, and become one of the great industrialists of his era. Penson's contribution in designing this attractive bridge has gone unrecorded, but a statue of the man who carried out the modest stone work stands alongside the bridge.

The bridge was built in 1846, the first of three in the County, and has a span of ninety feet (27.5m). The only plaque is a cast iron triangle stating the weight restrictions, bolted to the parapets. The ironwork was cast at Hawarden works. The restriction is still valid, confining the bridge to light traffic, which should ensure that the structure does not collapse. The problems caused by rust is a very different matter, and upkeep is going to be high if this and the other bridges are to survive.

Pont Brynderwen, 164952 (136)

The present iron bridge, a little downstream from the village of Aber-miwl, was built in 1852 to replace a wooden structure further downstream that was washed away by floods a year earlier. This bridge, the second to be designed by Penson, was cast at the Brymbo Steel Works, and has a span of one hundred and nine feet (33m). The arch is made up of iron letters similar to those found on Waterloo Bridge at Betws-y-coed. One has to scramble down the river bank to get a good view of this remarkable bridge, and to read the words which state:

This second bridge in the County of Montgomeryshire was erected in the year 1852.

The bridge, when I last saw it, was deteriorating rapidly and unless the rusting ironwork is treated soon, it is unlikely to survive.

Felindre Bridge, 943389 (136)

This is not an iron structure, but it is a grade 2 listed bridge. It was built by Penson around 1826 to gain access to 'Mount Severn' house. It has a single segmental arch, with the parapets curving outwards and terminating in piers. Vaussoirs with a band course over them make this an attractive bridge.

Caerhywel Bridge, 198981 (136)

The timber bridge at Caerhywel was destroyed in the floods of 1851, and a suspension bridge took its place. Penson voiced concern about its strength, and a few years later it collapsed under the weight of three loaded lime wagons, with some loss of life. Penson's original plan for a third iron bridge was then approved, and the building was completed in 1858. It is the widest of the three bridges, and again the ironwork was supplied by the Brymbo Works.

The bridge consists of two arches supported on dressed stone abutments and a central pier. A metal girder bridge has recently been slung across the top, controlled by traffic lights. The structure could not withstand the weight of present day traffic, and although an eyesore it is the price that has to be paid to preserve the original bridge.

Afon Efyrnwy and its Tributaries

There are a number of stone bridges in this area of Maldwyn but most are not of structural interest, having been built from the mid to late 19th century. Jervoise devoted only two pages to the area, and found only Pont Llangedwyn to be of any importance.

Pont Llangedwyn, 185239 (125)

The bridge spans Afon Tanant in a superb arch of elliptical shape, in a classical design. It spans nineteen yards (17.4m) and the nineteen foot (5.8m) wide roadway is of handsome proportions. Nothing is known about the designer and builder of this fine bridge, which appears to have been built towards the end of the 18th century. There is mention of an earlier bridge, Edward Llwyd recording a bridge 'over ye river Tanat' here, and Ogilby's route crossed here as well, but neither of them describe the earlier structures.

Pontrobert, 107127 (125)

The present bridge was rebuilt during the mid 19th century. It has two elliptical arches, spanning a distance of about thirty yards (9m), with semicircular cutwaters. Pontrobert was mentioned in a manorial rent roll of 1610, but it might not have been an important crossing at that time because Ogilby's route crossed at Pont Mathrafal, a couple of miles downstream.

Of the other bridges, Pont Dolanog which has a single arch ten feet wide appears to be much older than it really is, having been built of rough masonry. An interesting single arch, built of rough river boulders over Afon Gam at Llangadfan, (011097) gives the appearance of great age, but Jervoise did not consider any bridges on this river to be earlier than mid-19th century. This bridge has something of a rough elegance about it, and is well worth the detour from the main road to view it.

Little is known about Pont Ysgawrhyd *(Elderford)*, but Pont Sycoed is known to have been built in 1835.

Pont Llansanffraid is a handsome structure, thought to be from the early 19th century. Although much repaired, it is still a handsome structure of two arches and fine sweeping abutments. One of its notable features are a pair of half round recesses, some six feet (1.8m) by four feet (1.2m), built to match the cutwaters which are also rounded.

Cwm Tawe / *The Swansea Valley*

Pont Glais, 702008 (170)

There are no longer any stone bridges of interest on Afon Tawe between Glais and Abertawe *(Swansea)*. Progress demanded the removal of both of the fine structures of William Edwards – Wych Tree Bridge in Morriston, and Beauford Bridge further down.

The bridge at Glais is a solid structure of three arches built in 1806, with projecting keystones and a roadway twenty feet (6m) wide. The stepped cutwaters are a fine feature, as are the dressed stone parapets. The best viewpoint is from downstream because the upstream side carries a metal pathway and a number of unsightly pipes.

Pontardawe (Bridge), 724037 (170)

This fine arch of eighty feet (26m) span is not the one built by William Edwards on the same spot. Now bypassed and surrounded by concrete flyovers, it is worth a closer inspection, although it is not of a great age, and Jervoise chose to ignore it.

The original crossing was built by Edwards around 1765, and had one cylindrical opening in each haunch. These appear to have been filled in sometime before 1819 when T. Rees stated in his *Topography of South Wales* that the abutments were solid.

The present bridge shows no signs of such an infill, and there is no indication of widening underneath it either, which suggests that the old bridge was completely demolished during this one's construction. At well over twenty feet (6m) wide and built of dressed stone, it is a handsome arch. Apart from the inevitable neglect of the parapets, it is still in good condition.

Pont Offeiriad, 845145 (160)

This single arch structure has no special features, but for the fact that it was originally built for Adelina Patti, the opera singer, to connect her home at Craig y Nos with the railway station, which she also had built, at Penwyllt. It probably dated from the early 1880s, and although its name (The Parsons Bridge) is somewhat unclear, the fact that Madame Patti was a devoted Catholic would suggest that she had some influence in its naming. The extensive development of the Penwyllt quarries in recent years has resulted in the need for a stronger bridge, but this modern structure still carries the original name.

619907 (159)

This small, one arch, rusticated crossing over the Black Pill stream at Sgeti *(Sketty)* can now hardly be described as a bridge as little more than the arch remains. A photograph taken at the turn of the century confirms that it did at the time have abutments and parapets and was (wrongly as usual) called Roman Bridge.

Any attempt to date the bridge is purely speculative. It probably predates the fine tramway bridge of around 1840, just above it over a tributary, but a recent booklet on the archaeology of the area chose to ignore it, suggesting that it is of a much later date than its appearance leads us to believe. Although the arch is crudely built of flat stones, mortar has been used possibly at a later date. The area above the bridge is now part of the Clyne Valley Country Park, and there is ample room to view it, the best point being from the main Mumbles road.

The Llwchwr *(Loughor)* Estuary Bridges, 562981 (159)

In 1988 a fine new concrete bridge was built to replace the earlier ferroconcrete crossing of 1922. Prior to this a causeway and bridge, built in 1834, had become something of an improvement on the 'ford at low water', shown by Ogilby on his map. The timber bridge was, by all accounts, not the best of structures and soon became so unstable that coach drivers still preferred to use the ford.

The rail crossing alongside it is the only surviving timber viaduct in Wales to have been designed by Brunel. Built in the early 1850s, it consisted of seventeen timber pile piers and trusses, and a wrought iron opening section. By the late-19th century the opening had been replaced by a fixed span with iron, and later steel, used to replace the superstructure. The appearance of the bridge was much altered in 1981 when new timber piles were driven in, and jointed to the original Baltic yellow pine piers.

Pont Glanaman, 674138 (159)

Jervoise recorded Pont Glanaman as having 'corbelled parapets and two small semicircular flood openings' and a roadway of 'only eleven feet' (3.3m). When I arrived to inspect, I was far too late for the present bridge has a plaque stating that it was widened and rebuilt in 1936. Although the two flood openings have been retained, it bears little resemblance to the original bridge.

Pont-y-clerc, 621109 (159)

Malkin recorded, in 1804, a bridge built by William Edwards over Afon

Aman near the suburb of Betws in Rhydaman. Jervoise disagreed, stating that he was probably referring to Pont-y-clerc over Afon Llwchwr between Pantyffynnon and Ty-croes. Others doubt that this bridge is a survivor of Edwards' work, arguing that Jervoise's claim that the bridge's 'thin arch stones of the type used by Edwards' is not strong enough evidence.

This bridge can, however, stand on its own merit with a span of forty-five feet (13.7m) and a sixteen foot (5m) roadway. The most notable feature is the corbelled parapet, one of the very few remaining in Wales.

River Bridges of North-Eastern Wales

Caergwrle Packhorse Bridge, 307577 (117)

This bridge, the oldest over Afon Alun and probably in the district, is a typical example of the problem that faces those who attempt to conserve ancient bridges. This involves having to strike a happy medium between rendering the bridge safe, and carrying out so much repair as to virtually rebuild the structure. The bridge is situated at the end of Fellows Lane between Caergwrle and Hope, and is so narrow that the iron swing gate confines its use to pedestrians only. It consists of three arches over the river, with cutwaters and recesses, and a roadway of only four feet (1.2m) wide.

The causeway a little further east is made up of two arches, is some eighteen inches (45cm) wider, and of a later date. Built of river boulders, it has suffered from too much restoration, but is still unique and well worth seeking out.

295552 (171)

A packhorse bridge on Afon Cegidog, described by Jervoise as having a 'roadway of nearly five feet (1.5m), and a span of six yards (5.5m)'.

Gresford Lodge Bridge, 343553 (117)

It is unthinkable that Jervoise missed this bridge, but it is not named on the maps and judging by its dilapidated condition has been disused for many years. It may be the one recorded by Llwyd as 'Pont Resford'. The later crossing a little upstream has been swept away to make way for the new flyover.

The bridge has three arches, all overgrown with vegetation and showing signs of damage, and any track leading to it has long since disappeared. The earliest downstream side, some eight feet (2.4m) wide, has been widened by a further nine feet (2.7m), and the two sections can be seen from underneath. Access to this interesting ruin, for it can hardly be called anything else, is easy across the wasteground upstream.

Cooks Bridge, 383564 (117)

It is probable that this is the site of the bridge named by Llwyd as Pont Allington, and his Pont Rhyd Ithel, half a mile downstream is now known as Ithel's Bridge.

Worthenbury Bridge, 419461 (117)

Situated just inside Wales, this bridge deserves a mention having been built by H. J. Fairclough in 1872 in the vernacular style using yellow bricks.

Overton Bridge, 355427 (117)

According to Pennant, the first stone bridge at Overton was of 'two neat arches' and was built 'by the benevolence of Gwenhwyfar, daughter of Iorwerth Ddu of Pengwern near Llangollen', but he does not suggest a date.

Ogilby's route from Shrewsbury to Holywell crossed about a mile and a half below the present bridge, but there was a crossing at the site at the end of the 17th century, and this was mentioned by Llwyd. By his time, the bridge was in a bad state of repair and the building of a new one was attempted by Thomas Penson Senior. This ambitious single arch project collapsed (see Failures), and the present bridge was completed by his
son Thomas Junior, who went on to build the iron bridges of Montgomeryshire.

Jervoise describes Overton Bridge as having 'two semicircular arches, having rusticated voussoirs and a moulded string course around each arch'.

Pont-y-blew, 310383 (126)

A small bridge over Afon Ceiriog just east of Chirk shares its name with the nearby hamlet. It was mentioned by Pennant in 1773, and Jervoise found it little changed in 1931. He recorded a roadway eight feet (2.4m) wide and fourteen yards (12.8) long.

Pont-y-llan, Nantglyn, 004620 (116)

This little bridge near the church has two miniature arches and a splayed parapet.

Pontyglyndiffwys, 991444 (125)

This splendid single arch, sixty feet (18.2m) above Afon Geirw, was probably the one mentioned by Llwyd as Bont Newydd. A sketch by Gastineau was widely used in a number of books published during the mid-19th century. The local bard and playwrite, Twm o'r Nant, who earned his living as a haulage contractor, is reputed to have supplied the stone. Jervoise mentions the bridge only by name and does not give any details, its position in a romantic glen having failed to impress him. The exact time of construction is uncertain, the most probable date being in the 1780s.

During the Tithe Wars of the 19th century, which were caused by the insistence of the Church in England to levy taxes from the nonconformist Welsh farmers, Pontyglyn was the scene of a confrontation between these farmers and the ecclesiastical Bailiffs. The Bailiffs had come to seize stock from a farm in Llangwm, but were persuaded to leave empty handed having been dangled over the parapet. Sixty feet wasn't worth a cow!

Pont Dafydd, 046748 (116)

Situated in the town of Llanelwy *(St Asaph)*, the bridge is marked on the O.S. maps as an antiquity, and its cobbled roadway is now reserved for pedestrians only. The Dafydd in question was Bishop of St Asaph, and a document from the Botryddan Memoirs of 1630 state that: 'in yemoneths of June, July, August, September, and October, Pont Davyd Esgob was rebuilt anew'.

Jervoise expressed doubt that, 'this bridge is really so old', but agreed that it was situated on a very old site.

Llanelwy *(St Asaph)* Bridge, 036743 (116)

Both the old bridges in the town are bypassed by the A55, and this one over Afon Elwy was built by Joseph Turner in 1770. It was sketched by Gastineau in 1828.

It must have been widened, or perhaps completely rebuilt, as it is now twenty-four feet (7.3m) wide, which is much more than the normal width for a late 18th century bridge. There are five arches, seventy-eight yards (71m) long, the middle arch being the widest. A footbridge hides most of the upstream side.

Bridges of Afon Clwyd and its Tributaries

Pont Howkin, 121582 (116)

This bridge over Afon Clwyd, next to the car park in Ruthin, has suffered at the hands of the road planners. It was widened by having concrete beams buried into the roadway, and they protrude over each side. This is a common method of widening bridges where the arches are still considered strong enough to carry the extra traffic, and one can be forgiven for not expecting to find anything of interest under this pile of concrete. But those who can squeeze between the abutments and the toilets to reach the river bank will find three well preserved segmental arches of dressed stone. Jervoise records the width to be twenty-two feet (6.8m) but does not attempt a date, only to say that it was not the bridge which in 1781 was 'surrounded by flood and isolated all night'.

Pontrhydycilgwyn, 108605 (116)

One of the oldest bridges in the Vale of Clwyd, it is possible that it may have been built at the same time as Rhewl house, in 1634. Jervoise considered it had remained much as it was in Llwyd's time, and records that it had 'two segmental arches with triple arch rings of a very unusual type, the inner ones consisting of deep stones, the outer of flat slabs'.

He recorded a total span of twenty-two yards (20m) and a width of only nine feet (2.7m), with a cutwater and recess on each side. It had already been bypassed in the middle of the last century by the present bridge.

Bontuchel, 085578 (116)

The translation is 'tall bridge', and it is just that, but has no other notable feature. It probably dates from the mid-19th century.

Pont Rhuddlan, 022780 (116)

A bridge existed at Rhuddlan as early as 1281, and there is a great deal of documentary evidence that provides an interesting record of the crossing in the 14th century.

In 1326 Richard De Legh, a carpenter was assigned to repair it for a 'fee of four pence a day'. He must have fought a losing battle for the bridge at 'Rothelan was newly built' in 1331. Even this had a short life for in 1354 it was reported that it would 'soon fall unless repaired'. These were without doubt timber bridges and the present crossing, according to Pennant; 'appears to have been built or repaired in 1595'. He also remembers the date and 'the arms of William Hughes, the Bishop of St

189

Asaph at the time being cut into the battlements'.

Jervoise states that the bridge had two segmental arches and adds, 'they have double arch rings, the smaller one appears to be more ancient than the other, and its inner arch ring is chamfered and the upper part of the outer ring has been repaired with larger stones than were used for the rest of the arch, which gives the impression that this arch was repaired when the other one was rebuilt'. He suggests the smaller arch may be part of the 1595 structure, and that the large span is 19th century.

He recorded the total span in 1931 to be forty-five yards (41m) and the width was twenty-two feet (6.8m). The footway was even then being carried on iron brackets, and when I inspected the bridge, constant road resurfacing had lifted the roadway to the top of the stone parapets.

A new footbridge has now been constructed downstream, which makes life easier for pedestrians, but ruins the viewpoint from that area and puts paid to any attempt to photograph the castle through the arches.

Pontygwyddel, 953718 (116)

The 'Irish Bridge' is possibly named after Ogilby's route from London to Holyhead, which passed over it. Its two segmental arches have been widened and the remaining structure is not of a great age. Jervoise said it was an 'interesting structure', but does not explain his reasons, only that the single arch rings are built of stones of irregular sizes.

Pont Newydd, 013709 (116)

This bridge has two segmental arches, the second of a much later date and part of a rebuilding plan that was never completed. The roadway over this arch according to Jervoise was eighteen feet (5.5m) wide, but only nine feet (2.7m) over the older section. He also recorded it had a massive cutwater.

Pont-y-ddôl, 985725 (116)

Jervoise was rather vague about this bridge, which was unusual for him, and recorded that it 'is said to date from the sixteenth century'. He goes on to describe the two arches as 'three centred in form' and a total width of nine and a half feet (2.8m), and a span of forty yards (36.6m). He appears to have the date wrong because during the later part of the 19th century the inhabitants of this part were in conflict with the church over the payment of tithes. Many refused to pay and often had livestock and belongings taken in lieu by the church authorities.

The story often told in the area is that the bridge was built by the locals at their own expense in lieu for the payments due. It appears that the rural folk had the last word all the same, for the bridge was built straight into a rock on the other side of Afon Elwy, and it was several years before a road was constructed to connect with it.

Pont Perfa, 105633 (116)

Little is known about this bridge of two arches over Afon Clwyd at Llanynys, but it is considered to be of minor importance and is included among several lesser know and somewhat insignificant bridges in a book on ancient buildings of Clwyd.

The Bridges of Afon Dyfrdwy

Afon Dyfrdwy is known in English as the River Dee. This is probably due to the fact that its long estuary, and much of its latter length, forms the boundary between Wales and England. It rises some five miles west of Llyn Tegid *(Bala lake)*, and just before it flows into the largest sheet of natural water in Wales it is joined by Afon Twrch. Beyond the lake it receives Afon Tryweryn regulated by the still controversial Llyn Celyn, that aroused so much National feeling when it was created in the 1960s.

Afon Dyfrdwy supplies much of north-eastern Wales with its water, which is drawn out at intervals along its length, and for that reason it is a clean, fast flowing and attractive river.

There are few bridges of interest to the west and north of Llyn Tegid, and Jervoise did not consider any to be 'more than a century old'. A number were recorded by Edward Llwyd, but according to Pennant most were destroyed during a great flood in 1780. Richard Fenton states that so great was the floodwater, the lake did not clear for three years.

The oldest is probably 'Pont Lliw' at Llanuwchllyn which was built in 1852 and has two elliptical stone arches: Pont-y-Llan within the village is a girder bridge and bears the words, *Brimbo 1880*.

In the town of Bala, Pont Tryweryn, also known as Pont y Bala has four arches, and the original part could be as early as the mid-18th century, but the parapets have been rebuilt, and the roadway increased to eighteen feet (5.5m) wide.

Pont Mwnwgl-y-llyn, 930351 (125)

The river leaves the lake under this bridge, mentioned by both Llwyd and Pennant, which at one time carried the old drovers road over the Berwyn Range to Llangynnog. It still has three arches, the same number as the original, but it has been widened to seventeen feet (5.2m). It is thirty-five yards (32m) in length and is a solid attractive bridge which has lost its character to recent rebuilding.

Pont-fawr, Llandderfel, 982364 (125)

This bridge was also mentioned by Llwyd and Pennant, the latter recording that it had four arches which is also the present number. At fifty-five yards (50m) long it is a pleasant bridge to view from downstream, the upstream side having been widened to nineteen feet (5.8m). A certain amount of rebuilding work has taken place recently, and in order to straighten the sharp northern approach, a steel girder has been built into one side of the arch, a most distracting feature, but the most acceptable method of straightening corners. It has kept its character well despite all this 'butchering', and is well worth a closer inspection.

A number of land arches on the southern approach were built at a much later date to cope with the floodwaters. Dating the bridge is difficult, as it has neither an inscription or any special features, but the older downstream side is probably late-18th century.

Pontcilan, 022375 (125)
The bridge was described by Pennant as 'a bridge of two arches over deep and black water', and Jervoise noted that the description 'applies equally well at the present day'. The bridge has since undergone many changes, but when I visited it on a warm summer's day the water was still 'deep and black'.

Jervoise noted that the parapets had been rebuilt by using light girders overhanging the face of the bridge, and he was of the opinion that they did not spoil its appearance. Since then there has been considerable restructuring, which has resulted in new parapets of stone slabs set on their sides and topped with railings. They are much higher than average for a bridge of this type; no doubt the Council is well aware of the danger of the 'deep and dark water'.

The remains of the iron parapets can still be seen, and the arches remain almost untouched. The width is now less than the fourteen feet (4.3m) measured by Jervoise, the stone slabs taking up about three feet (90cm) of the roadway. The span is thirty-two yards (29.2m).

Pont Llandrillo, 035372 (125)
This imposing bridge over Afon Ceidiog has three segmental arches and the rustic appearance that one expects of stone bridges in this part of Wales. It is however not of a great age, and has been widened on the upstream side by about ten feet (3m).

Pont Cynwyd, 053412 (125)
This lofty bridge of four segmental arches is by far the most important on the upper stretches of Afon Dyfrdwy, Jervoise considering it a 'very imposing structure'. It spans sixty-five yards (59m) with a width of eleven feet (3.3m), and recesses over the cutwaters. This bridge is in its original state, and in remarkable condition. It probably dates from the end of the 19th century.

Pont Baker, 045437 (125)
This bridge over Afon Alwen was named by Llwyd as Pontarddwyryd,

and the present name is probably attributed to the builder of the present crossing. It is a fine bridge of two obtusely pointed arches spanning thirty-five yards (32m) and around eleven feet (3.3m) in width. There are recesses over the cutwaters which could be what was retained from the earlier bridge when the arches were rebuilt.

Pont Corwen, 069433 (125)
Pont Corwen is the longest on the upper Dyfrdwy, spanning a distance of one hundred and seven yards (99m). There are at present seven arches but only two, or possibly three, serve for the passage of floodwater.

There was a bridge here in the 16th century, Camden recording a stone crossing in 1577. The one described by Pennant had six arches, which he considered to be 'a handsome bridge', which was also mentioned by Llwyd. The bridge, which today still carries the A5 trunk road is the result of much rebuilding and patching. Jervoise recorded a plaque with the date 1704 on the downstream parapet. He considered the original width to be about twelve feet (3.6m) but it is by now a wide twenty-two feet (6.8m). It is not an attractive bridge, any special features it once possessed having been sacrificed to the needs of modern traffic.

The iron bridge that crosses the river a little downstream is recent, replacing a footbridge.

Pont Carrog, 115435 (125)
The bridge at Carrog is illustrated by Jervoise in his book, and appears to have changed little since then, apart from some repointing to the parapets. He considered it to be one of the finest on the upper stretches of the river, and its five arches are an attractive sight when viewed from downstream. It spans sixty-two yards (57m) by twelve feet (3.6m) wide, but it is doubtful if all of the present structure dates from 1661, which is what the slate plaque that has been built into one of the downstream recesses informs us. Each cutwater has a recess, which have all been rebuilt, and only one retains an original stone seat.

Pont Llangollen, 225422 (117)
Had it not been subjected to considerable repairs and restoration, this bridge could be considered among the oldest in North Wales. According to Pennant it was 'founded by John Trefor, Bishop of St Asaph who died in 1357'. There was an even earlier bridge because a grant of poundage for three years was made to Roger De Mortuo Mari 'in aid of the repair and maintenance of his bridge at Thlangothlan', in 1282.

Leyland describes it as 'a great stone bridge over the Dee River', and

Llwyd states that it was repaired in 1656. It has also been reported that this date was at one time to be found carved on the parapet. The arms of Bishop Trefor were reputed to have been found on a stone during repairs in 1873. At this time, a stone with the figures 1131 and the letters W.S. were also discovered.

An additional arch was built to allow the railway to pass underneath in 1863, and the bridge was widened to twice its original width in 1873. Further work was carried out as late as the mid 1960s and little, if any, of the original structure remains unchanged.

Jervoise describes the bridge as having 'four arches, pointed in shape with chamfered arch rings built in two orders'. The width is now twenty feet (6.1m) and there are recesses over the triangular cutwaters.

According to the old rhyme, Llangollen Bridge 'was one of the seven wonders' of Wales. There is a good viewing point from both up and downstream, and during the annual International Eisteddfod the bridge is the focal point of much merriment.

King's Bridge, Llangollen, 198432 (125)
This is a high and handsome stone bridge of five arches, three over Afon Dyfrdwy and two over the canal, built in 1905. The reason for its construction was to connect the A542 with the A5 without having to detour through Llangollen.

Chain Bridge, Llangollen, 203435 (117)
This small suspension bridge over Afon Dyfrdwy just below Kings Bridge is restricted to pedestrians, having been in and out of repair many times since it was built in 1928. The first crossing on the site, again a suspension bridge, was built in 1814 to carry coal from the canal to the A5. It was washed away in 1820, and there was no real need for another bridge until the present shaky structure was slung across to serve the hotel on the northern side.

Bangor Bridge, 388455 (117)
This superb bridge is well worthy of its classification on the O.S. Maps as an antiquity, but regrettably little is known about its early history. We know it saw some form of action in the civil war when, according to William Maurice, it was 'betrayed to Colonel Mitton' on February 15th, 1644.

We also know it was repaired a few years later with Pennant recording an unusual plaque to that effect, but whether or not this was a complete rebuilding is a mystery. Even assuming that this was the case, it has received little or no alteration since, and its red sandstone has acquired a fine weathered appearance.

There are five three centred arches, with triple arch rings built in three orders. Its most unusual feature is its rectangular cutwaters which also have recesses at road level.

It spans seventy-six yards (70m) and is under eleven feet (3.3m) wide, but no longer carries modern traffic.

Holt Bridge, 412544 (117)

There was an important crossing of Afon Dyfrdwy as early as the 15th century according to William of Worcester, and Leyland recorded 'a great stone bridge on the Dee river' in the 'tòun of Holt'. Pennant, who passed in 1778, described the bridge as having 'ten arches, with a vestige of a guard house in the middle'. He mentioned that the date 1345 had been preserved over the third arch from the Welsh bank, known as the Lady arch, but Jervoise was very sceptical of such an early date. The bridge replaced a ferry, the rent for this being twenty-six shillings in 1315.

The bridge is one of only two surviving (the other is at Monmouth) that had a fortification on the bridge itself. In the case of Holt bridge, this was in the form of a drawbridge, probably situated on the third arch from the Welsh side. Jervoise mentions an additional arch ring halfway up the parapet, and suggest that this unique feature had no useful purpose and that the built up section served as the drawbridge. He concludes that the arch beneath is therefore of a 'much later date'.

The bridge featured in a civil war skirmish when the Parliamentarian troops rushed the bridge and: 'by placinge ladders to the toppe of the drawbridge and cutting the ropes' gained 'accesse to the gates'.

The date of construction of the present bridge is the subject of considerable speculation because there has been some rebuilding, apart from filling in the drawbridge gap. But the red sandstone has weathered a great deal over the years and it is no longer possible to identify the earlier parts. An illustration by Gastineau from 1828 shows a bridge of eight arches, which Jervoise confirmed. He also gave the measurements as ninety-two yards (84m) span and about fourteen feet (4.3m) in width with eight cutwaters and recesses.

This is one of the most important historical bridges in North Wales, and has been the subject of much sketching including a fine engraving by George Pickering in 1917.

The bridges of Pembrokeshire

Llanglydwen bridge, 180267 (158)
This bridge has a single pointed arch and circular openings in the haunches and is very similar to the bridge at Cwm Miles. It was probably built at about the same time and possibly by the same builder. A great deal of patching up has taken place on the parapets over the years, with no attempt at conformity. The bridge is in bad condition, and cannot be viewed from the river.

Pont Llawhaden, 075172 (158)
An insignificant crossing of four semicircular arches, forty-two yards (38.5m) long and fifteen feet (4.6m) wide.

Pont Cwm Miles, 164223 (158)
Due to private land surrounding the bridge on three sides, and a number of trees on the other, it is not possible to see the structure at its best. It has a high single arch and circular openings which appear to carry flood water rather than reduce construction pressure, as no attempt has been made to level out the approaches which rise sharply to the crest of the arch.

Pont Trevaughan, 201163 (158)
This stone bridge of three arches has now been bypassed but is still retained in good condition. The new structure carries the name of 'Pont Pontiac', which is something of a contradiction in terms.

Haverfordwest Old Bridge, 955159 (158)
The old bridge is so named in order to distinguish it from its more recent neighbour a little way downstream. There was a bridge at this point as early as the year 1378, when one Richard Lagham sought to obtain rents from it.

The present bridge displays a long inscription set into the tower on the upstream side stating that it was built in 1726, repaired in 1829, and widened in 1848. The four semicircular arches span some thirty-eight yards (35m), and the width of twenty-three feet (7m) is entirely taken up by the roadway, the pavement being carried on a metal footway resting on large concrete slabs on the downstream side.

The river flows over a weir a little below the bridge, and a pleasant shopping area and pathways between the two bridges provide a good viewing point, although the catwalk is distracting. The best position to see the old bridge is from a rather confined area upstream.

The inscription on the plaque, as is often the case when they relate to the history of a bridge, has been carved at different times. It is among the longest carved stone plaques on a Welsh bridge, surpassed only by the one on Builth Wells bridge. It reads,

> This bridge was erected at the sole expense of Sr John Phillips of Picton Castle, Bart, Anno. 1726. Michael Prust Esq. Mayor in memory where of this was set up by the Mayor and Council.

The later inscription reads,

> Repaired by order of the mayor and corporation A.D. 1829 in the tenth year of the reign of his majesty George the fourth who passed over the bridge on his return from Ireland the 13th day of September 1821.

The last inscription reads,

> This bridge was widened and repaired in the year 1848 under the direction of the Magistrates of the County of the town of Haverfordwest at the expense of the said County.

Sir Richard Colt Hoare sketched the bridge possibly as early as 1793 when he first visited the area, and published it as a print in 1806. It depicts the bridge with the tower in position and very similar to its present form, the later widening and repairs blending well with the original structure.

The Bosherton Bridges, O.S. Ref?
A number of small but very attractive stone bridges can be found spanning the well known Bosherton Lily ponds in the south of the peninsula. Most are of mid to late 19th century origin, and were built by the Stackpole estate. Those that form part of the footpath around the ponds are worth seeing.

The most interesting is the eight arch low bridge that carried the track between Stackpole Quay and the Home Farm. The estate is part of the Cawdor enterprise who dammed the stream to create the ponds almost two hundred years ago. The energetic can see all the crossings by undertaking the lengthy walk around the pools which is best done when the lilies are in bloom.

Nevern Bridge (Pont Nyfer), 083399 (145)
Although the wall below the bridge has been recently rebuilt, the crossing described by Jervoise as 'attractive' remains much as he saw it

198

apart from the inevitable patching up of the parapets. It dates from the early 19th century, has two arches with double arch rings, and a massive cutwater. It spans twenty yards (18.3m) and has a width of about ten feet (3m).

Pont Treseli, 252400 (145)
This single arch bridge over Afon Cuch has two openings in the haunches similar to Pont Cenarth (see Dyffryn Teifi Bridges), which was possibly built at the same time by the same builder. The roadway is eighteen feet wide, a generous width for a bridge somewhat off the beaten track. It is an attractive crossing and well worth a detour to see.

Those who are prepared to risk their cars along the very narrow road up to Cwm Cuch will find Pont Cuch to be only ten feet (3m) wide, and with a weathered appearance. The next one up is Pont Wedwst, and further up in Cwm Morgan, where the road is even narrower, there are a few more old, but by no means exceptional, bridges.

Pont Hywel, 129275 (158)
The road to the bridge is well signposted because of a nearby craft shop, but the bridge itself, which is one of the oldest in the area, has been badly mutilated. Jervoise recorded two semicircular arches with recesses and a plaque which stated,

> This bridge was rebuilt by John Mapps Rsq, Insbector Ao Do 1747.

Since then the parapets have been removed and replaced by a wire fence, and the recesses filled in with concrete. The plaque has disappeared. The arches which span twelve yards (11m) and are nine feet (2.7m) in width still remain, but with a seven ton weight restriction, its future looks bleak.

Cwm Gwaun
Cwm Gwaun is steep and wooded and its roads are so narrow that only those who care little for their motor vehicles will venture along them. Jervoise recorded two bridges: Pontfaen, which is marked as such on the maps, but which is known locally as Picton Mill bridge, and Cilrhedyn, which is also named on the maps. He described Picton Mill bridge as having 'two obtusely pointed arches' twelve feet (3.6m) wide, and Cilrhedyn Bridge as having 'two segmental arches' and a nine foot (2.7m) roadway. Both bridges were built of 'very rough masonry'.

Cutty Bridge, 939189 (157)

This is a much repaired two arch bridge that still retains some of its original structure. The two recesses are original which proves that the width of seventeen feet (5.2m) has not been obtained by widening. The approaches are sharp at both ends, which no doubt accounts for the new stonework on the parapets. The bridge gives its name to the small hamlet nearby.

The Bridges of Caerfyrddin *(Carmarthenshire)*

Pont Spwdwr, 436059 (159)

This ancient bridge of five pointed arches and one segmental arch was considered by Jervoise to be 'the most ancient bridge remaining in South Wales'. He mentions six pointed arches, of which only two are over Afon Gwendraeth Fach, the remainder serving as flood arches. The smallest arch on the south-westerly side is segmental and has possibly been rebuilt since Jervoise inspected it in 1931.

The bridge is now bypassed, and two iron stanchions prevent any wheeled traffic from crossing.

The date of construction is uncertain, but in 1571 one David Vaughan of Trimsaran left the sum of forty shillings for its repair. A further twenty shillings were left for the same purpose by Griffith ap William Vaughan, his nephew, sixteen years later. Ogilby's route to Tyddewi *(St David's)* passed over Pont Spuddorey. The overall length, which includes the approaches, is seventy yards (64.2m) and it is ten feet (3m) wide with recesses over the cutwaters.

It can be viewed from the bypass bridge or from downstream, but rapidly growing willow trees is now making the latter position difficult. It is marked on O.S. maps as an antiquity, and surely deserves to be treated as such.

Pont Rhyd Rymus, 643372 (146)

This bridge over Afon Cothi was built in 1777 but has been rebuilt in parts, according to Jervoise. He recorded that it had three segmental arches spanning thirty-three yards (30m) and a roadway of ten feet (3m) with recesses over the cutwaters.

Pont Abergorlech, 585335 (146)

Jervoise considered this to be the most interesting bridge over Afon Cothi. He described the arches as being 'very distorted' and partly rebuilt on the upstream side. He stated that two of the three arches were pointed and the other segmented, and that the older arches may date from as early as the sixteenth century. He felt that the newer arch was 'only about a hundred years old'. He also mentioned a plaque with a faint inscription in the northern recess which read,

This bridge was mended by John Jones 1794,
and that the last digit was reversed.

He recorded the total span as twenty-nine yards (26.5m) with a width of eight feet (2.4m).

The bridge has undergone considerable repairs in recent years with all the arches and the parapet being rebuilt or re-pointed. Although the basic shape of the arches remain much as Jervoise described them, the whole character of bridge has been lost. The stone inscription is no longer in place.

Pont Llandeilo, 628220 (159)

It is possible that a stone bridge crossed Afon Tywi at Llandeilo as early as 1577, but by the mid-18th century there was only a ferry with a charge of half a penny per person or horse load. A bridge, reputed to have been built by the Edwards family of Pontypridd, was completed in 1779.

In 1819 it was described by Rees as 'a substantial stone bridge of modern erection, but owing to miserable parsimony it has been made so narrow that a carriage cannot pass upon it without some danger'.

The present structure was started in 1844, involving forty workmen. The construction soon proved to be a slow and costly venture, and a major setback occurred in October 1846 when 'part of the centre was carried off' when flood water swept away the timber structure along with five men, (see Floods and Failures). By the time the bridge was completed in 1848 the cost had risen from an estimated six thousand to twenty-two thousand pounds.

The venture however was a remarkable achievement that was described by G. Eyre Evans a little later as 'probably the finest one arch bridge in Wales'. It was also the longest single span in Wales, topping William Edwards' bridge at Pontypridd by five feet (1.5m), and remains the longest stone built span. The building involved a long and high approach road to level off as much as possible of the steep hill leading to the town, which included a fine four centred arch in the abutments. The building blocks are enormous, and are all dressed to a flat surface. The parapet stones are rounded because it was fashionable at the time. The centre of the upstream parapet carries the inscription in large letters, *erected 1848*.

An inscription on the south side of the downstream parapet is something of a mystery. Although cut well enough into the stone, it reads in a line several feet in length, and across a number of stones. It was carved possibly some time after the bridge was completed.

It is in Welsh, perhaps because the locals were unhappy with the English only inscription. It reads:

Pont Llandeilo, Codwyd i gymeryd lle hen bont saith bwa 1779.

202

(Llandeilo Bridge, Erected to replace the old seven arch bridge of 1779).

Just above this inscription, a bronze plaque carries the following inscription:

Old Bridge Llandeilo 1779. This single arch bridge of 145 ft (span) was erected in 1848 to replace the old 7 arch bridge, architect W. Williams. This plaque was presented by T. Thomas Beechwood Llandeilo, Chairman of Llandeilo District Council 1948-49.

This plaque is the only one of which I am aware that was installed to commemorate the hundredth anniversary of a bridge.

Pont Llandeilo is well worth viewing, preferably from the river bank so as to gain the full effect of this remarkable high sweeping arch.

Pont Alltycafan, 387392 (145)

This high and handsome stone bridge ranks among the finest single arched structures in the old county of Caerfyrddin. The openings have been well designed and positioned so as to lighten what would otherwise have been a very heavy and robust crossing. The upstream valley is a well known beauty spot, but the closure of the woollen mills around the bridge has resulted in the area taking on something of a run down appearance. There are now far fewer photographers who are prepared to muddy their shoes and scratch their hands by scrambling down to the river side to get that special shot through the arch.

The saga of its construction is recorded on the sandstone plaque on the west parapet, which reads:

This bridge was built, the approaches formed and the road from Rhyd Fach to 'Llandussil' made, through the exertions of John Lloyd Davies Esquire of Blaendyffryn, who from a conviction of its benifit to the county projected the work and proquired the money necessary to execute it in the years 1839 = 40 = 41.

It is hard to believe that such a bridge took such a long time to build, and by all accounts the good squire had some difficulty in 'proquiring' sufficient funds. Having finally completed the work he made sure posterity would not be allowed to forget his contribution.

Pont Felin Cwrrws, 353412 (145)

An insignificant little bridge, but worthy of mention because of the now rather worn plaque it carries, which reads:

This bridge was erected and the approaches to it made in the year 1840, partly by funds raised from the county of Cardigan, and partly by subscriptions from individuals in this (and) the adjoining counties of Carmarthen and Pembroke.

The Bridges of Dyffryn Tywi

Pont Llandeilo Rwnws, 494483 (159)

Afon Tywi was crossed by a ford at this point until a bridge was built around 1786. The travel writer Malkin states that the builder was David Edwards. The centre arch of three was badly damaged by flood in 1931, shortly before Jervoise arrived to inspect it. He states that: 'owing to the excellence of the masonary the arches stood firm'; another tribute to the building skills of the Edwards' family of Pontypridd. Jervoise also mentioned it cost six hundred pounds to repair the damage. A plaque states,

> Built 1786, rebuilt 1933 after flood in 1931 T.W. Wishlake, Arolygwr y Sir.

Pont Abergwili, 434210 (159)

The original bridge of four arches was rebuilt in 1769 and again in 1802. The present crossing, which dates from around that time, has a single segmented arch and circular openings in the haunches.

Pont Llanymddyfri, 762347 (146)

There were many wooden bridges at this site although Leyland only recorded, and cryptically at that, a ford: 'which there often times dronith in winter men for lakke of a bridge'. Ogilby crossed at this point and did not record a bridge. The 1773 *Journal of the House of Commons* however, referred to a petition concerning the rebuilding of 'Llandovery Bridge', and stated that the new bridge erected in 1772 on the foundations of a previous bridge had already fallen down. Permission was given for a new bridge, which again must have been wooden as it constantly needed repairing and had, by 1832, cost the county so much that it was decided to erect a Chain Suspension Bridge. Phylip Thomas of Ynysangharad near Pontypridd designed it, and based it upon Telford's masterpiece over the Menai Straits. The bridge was badly needed since coaches had for some years been travelling a mile (1.6km) further upstream to the stone bridge at Dolauhirion, rather than risking the unsafe wooden structure.

The new bridge was called the Chain Bridge, and only had a short lifespan since it was removed in 1873, probably because it was too narrow. It was in good enough condition to allow it to be re-erected in Buckland by the Gwynne Holland family of Gwynfe. The bridge that replaced it has three stone arches, and is some fifty-eight yards (53m) long and twenty-two feet (6.7m) wide, which made it wide enough even for modern day traffic. It was however felt to be too narrow to allow pavements, and a controversial tubular steel bridge has been erected alongside for this purpose. The controversy arose from the choice of material and also the general design of the metal bridge. It towers above the stone bridge, obstructing the fine view of the old bridge from the river bank. It was also considered to be out of character with the rural setting. The objections were upheld by the local council, but they were overruled. Although the stone bridge was not of architectural importance, this was another fine example of bureaucrats ignoring the wishes of a small rural community.

Pont Dolauhirion, 762361 (146)

This bridge, known originally as Dolhir, was considered by Jervoise to be the finest on the upper Tywi, and by many others to be the best surviving bridge by William Edwards. There has been some doubt about the actual date of construction, but it is now accepted to be 1773. It appears today to be an unusual place to erect such a fine bridge, but the presence of earlier wooden bridges indicates the importance of the crossing which was on the road to Llanbedr Pont Steffan *(Lampeter)*.

The single segmental arch is twenty-eight yards (25.6m) long, a good deal less than his more famous work at Pontypridd, and has one circular opening in each haunch. The roadway is twelve feet (3.6m) wide.

The bridge needs to be viewed from the river bank, but the number of trees on both sides prove to be something of a distraction.

Pontardywi, 695286 (146)

Travellers over this bridge, a mile west of Llangadog, cannot fail to see the plaque on the upstream parapet with the large figures, '1819'. Jervoise does not mention it, which means that it was probably installed after his visit. The bridge has three large segmental arches, and two smaller ones serving as flood arches on the eastern side which gives it a somewhat lopsided appearance. The pointed cutwaters are attractive, and although the masonry is now showing signs of weathering it has received no other rebuilding other than the inevitable patching of the parapets. The roadway is a handsome nineteen feet (5.8m) wide, and it is worthy of more than just a glance.

The Bridges of Dyffryn Teifi

Afon Teifi is one of Wales' best known salmon rivers, and for much of its length forms the boundary between Ceredigion *(Cardigan)* and Caerfyrddin *(Carmarthen)*. On its journey from the high moorland of mid-Wales to the sea at Aberteifi it receives several tributaries, none of which have bridges of any particular significance. Of those that span Afon Teifi itself, Jervoise did not consider any on the upper reaches to be of any interest, but they are nevertheless worth recording, and are typical of the mid-19th century bridges to be found in west Wales.

Pontrhydfendigaid, 731665 (135)
This, the first stone bridge of any significance over Afon Teifi, is a 'humped' single arch bridge built of small outcrop stones. It has no special features and is well under one hundred and fifty years old.

Pont Einion, 672614 (146)
The present three arch bridge over Afon Teifi, on the A485 between Tregaron and Llanilar, was built by the local builders John and David Rees in 1805, and has seen much patching up since that time. It does not have any special features, but many stories relate to previous bridges at this site. One suggests that the first bridge was built in 1281 by Einion Sais, the Abbot of Ystrad Fflur *(Strata Florida)*, and that it was the first stone bridge in the county. Other stories maintain that the Einion in question was a local man who had lived away for many years, and almost drowned while crossing the river on his return. As a result, he built a stone bridge. What is certain is that a number of bridges have been built at this point since the middle ages.

Pont Gogoian, 642546 (135)
This is a magnificent stone bridge with a high wide arch in the middle, supported by two smaller arches on each side. Regrettably there is no inscription and even Jervoise, who admitted that it was 'imposing', was not prepared to comment on a possible time of construction. He mentions a distance of forty-five yards (41m) and a width of eleven feet (3.3m), which is now just over twelve feet (3.6m), the parapets having been rebuilt in the original stone some time since his visit, and made narrower to gain an extra foot (30cm) of road width. The south arch has also been rebuilt quite recently, this time in new stone with quite distracting effect. It is best viewed from the banks of the deep and dark pool just below.

Pont Llanfair Clydogau, 623514 (135)

Jervoise mentions this bridge, but only refers to it having the same width as Pont Gogoian. It is smaller, having only three arches, neatly built with attractive stepped cutwaters.

Pont Llanybydder, 520442 (135)

This bridge is a fine example of a mid-19th century crossing, and has three segmental arches.

Pont Llanfihangel-ar-arth, 457403 (135)

This high and wide single arch is attractive, but has no special features and dates from the mid-19th century.

Henllan Bridge, 356401 (145)

Llwyd records that 'there is one only large stone bridge upon ye river Tivy', and it is probable that it was at the site of the present crossing. A sandstone plaque on the outside of the east parapet has the initials, Edze.JD.JT.JE.JJ.1744. This was probably removed from the earlier bridge during rebuilding work, but the present structure has recesses over the cutwaters, and could possibly include much of the earlier bridge. It has three segmental arches spanning forty yards (36.6m) and a width of fifteen feet (4.6m).

Pont Castellnewydd Emlyn *(Newcastle Emlyn Bridge)*, 308409 (145)

There is little historical evidence relating to this bridge, but it has been widened by about seven feet (2.1m) on the downstream side. This work probably included considerable rebuilding, which involved strengthening the bridge by filling in the upstream recesses, and raising the parapets, which had been described by Rowlandson in 1797 as being extremely low. The width is now nineteen feet (5.3m) and the span is forty yards (36.6m), and the bridge has three segmental arches.

Pont Cenarth, 269416 (145)

The present bridge is an imposing structure of three segmental arches with large circular openings above the piers. It was sketched by Henry Gastineau and appeared in his *Wales Illustrated* in 1830, but there is surprisingly no written evidence regarding the time of its construction, or the builder. It has been suggested that it was the work of David Edwards, possibly on the grounds of the circular openings, but most consider that it was built during the later years of the 18th century and David Edwards was at that time building the bridge at Newport.

It is the only stone bridge to be built on this site, the earlier crossing a little downstream being a wooden structure. Jervoise offers no information other than to record that it was fifteen feet (4.6m) wide and forty-five yards (41m) in length. It has not been widened, but the downstream abutment has been straightened to ease the sharp corner, a common enough practice that was often carried out by inserting concrete beams, lengthwise, alongside the parapet.

The area around the bridge is a tourist attraction, with falls and a water mill upstream. There is a small fishing museum on the northern side and a deep pool that was once used as a communal sheep washing place, which is now much frequented by fishermen, and also as a site for coracle demonstrations.

Pont Llechryd, 217437 (145)

It is remarkable that this bridge has survived with only minor flood damage as the river has often flowed over the parapets, which Jervoise described as being 'unusually low'. A plaque dated 1656 has survived from an earlier bridge, and was built into one of the cutwaters during rebuilding, but regrettably there is no record of when this took place.

Malkin, in 1804, mentioned that the bridge was covered in ivy 'which creeps over its parapets', and Rees in 1819 described it as 'an ancient ivy mantled bridge'. The ivy continued to flourish well into the present century, as photographs prove, but most has now been removed. The length is fifty-seven yards (52m) which is spanned by six segmental arches, and a width of ten feet (3m). There are recesses over the cutwaters.

Pont Aberteifi *(Cardigan Bridge)*, 177458 (145)

This is the last bridge over Afon Teifi, where, in a translation of the words of the poet Cynan,

It arrives in full majesty
Past Cardigan town to be wed to the sea.

There appears to have been a bridge here when Geraldus Cambrensis and Archbishop Baldwin crossed over during their journey in 1188, but there is no further record until 1606. In 1647 the House of Commons were petitioned by the inhabitants of the two counties who pointed out:

The bridge over the river Tivey, which was built about eight years ago at a cost of £1,500, has lately been broken down by the enemy (this was during the Civil War) to the great hindrance to trade between the two counties . . . Pray that £500 may be speedily levied

209

out of the delinquent estates in the county for the purpose.'

The bridge was presumably repaired, but in 1726 further work was required and at least one arch was rebuilt. A sandstone plaque was installed with the words:

This arch was built in ye year 1726, W. Jones.

The bridge described by Meyrick in 1808 had seven arches, a number confirmed by Rees, but higher up river than the original. The present bridge has only five arches, which means that it must therefore have been built after this date or, as is more likely, the other two arches (possibly one from each end) were removed and replaced by the present river walls. The bridge shows widening by about three feet (90cm) on the downstream side to a width of fifteen feet (4.6m), and during this time the plaque was removed and placed in its present position on the outside of the upstream parapet. The length is eighty-six yards (79m) according to Jervoise, who also recorded 'five massive cutwaters upstream, three of which have recesses'.

The slate parapet stones in one of the recesses are covered in lovers initials going back to the turn of the century. Three of the downstream arches have recently been rebuilt using local slate, with double arch rings, and look very attractive. Pedestrians no longer need to scurry from one recess to another to avoid the traffic, since a new footbridge was built in 1976.

Bridges of Ceredigion *(Cardigan)*

Pont yr Offeiriad *(Parson's Bridge)*, 749791 (135)

The bridge is considered important enough to be marked on the new O.S. maps, but the present structure differs considerably from the one described by Rees in 1809 as:

> a footbridge of the rudest kind consisting of little more than a plank or beam of wood, with only a slight handrail for defence.

There was little improvement when Borrow viewed the river from it almost forty years later, but the present day traveller who wishes to venture into this wild area can rest assured that his safety is taken into consideration after the construction of a solid metal bridge. Its name is derived from its use by the local clergy who travelled across Afon Rheidol from Ysbyty Cynfyn to Ystumtuen, to conduct services during the heyday of lead mining in the area.

Pont Llanychaem, 589788 (135)

A lattice girder bridge over Afon Ystwyth, built in 1872 by Evans and Jenkins of Aberystwyth to a design by G.H. Thomas of Liverpool. A slate plaque on the parapet reads,

> This bridge was erected by public subscriptions through the exertions of W.E. Richards Esq. R.A. Bryneithin and his friends, and the stone was laid by Mrs Davies Tan y Bwlch January 16th 1872.

Pontrhydygroes, 741728 (135)

The bridge at the ford of the cross has one large arch, but it is not the one described by the historian Meyrick as 'a neat stone bridge'. Jervoise only states that it 'appears to be of much later date', and did not attempt to read the plaque which would have confirmed his statement. Part of it is now broken as a result of a lorry crashing into the parapet, but the inscription in part Welsh and part English read:

> Rhydygroes, adaeladwyd gan Gynghor Sirol Ceredigion Ad 1893 Syrveyor R. Lloyd, Contractor Capt, J. Owen.

The plaque was inserted on the condition that it did not cost more than twenty shillings.

Pont y Pump, 361540 (145)

This small bridge over Nant Haen in the village of Llangrannog is so nearly covered in tarmac as to be invisible. Its only claim to fame is its name (which means The Bridge of Five) and it carries a bilingual plaque stating that it was built in 1884, and that J. Owen, T. Evans, J. Davies, S.G. Griffiths and D. Jones, were responsible. It appears that all five gave the same estimate to build it, as they did not wish to undercut each other. The result was that each was given a small section of the bridge to build, hence its name.

There are dozens of small stone bridges scattered through the area, some of which have inscriptions in the form of dates and names which are worth a passing glance, but have no other special features. Of the lattice girder bridges most are modern and of no great interest, but will often carry plaques similar to the one on the B4343 between Llanddewibrefi and Tregaron, which states that it was built by Cardigan County Council in 1896.

Pont Blaen, 826755 (135)

The old coaching route from Rhaeadr to Aberystwyth crossed Afon Yswyth at Blaen-y-cwm over a bridge described by Malkin as having 'elegant proportions', and by Jervoise as 'an unusually fine structure for such an outlandish place'! It was built in 1783 at the expense of Thomas Johnes of Hafod by his personal designer, a Mr Bauldwin of Bath.

Its single segmental arch spans a rocky gorge with a span of fourteen yards, and a width of fifteen feet. There is surprisingly no inscription, but the coat of arms of Thomas Johnes of three crows and an inverted chevron, on a sandstone plaque, was built into the outside of two pillars in the middle of the parapets. They can therefore only be viewed from the river bank, and although Jervoise described them as 'quite distinct', the years since have taken their toll, and what remains of the raised carving would benefit from a clean up.

The bridge has been well constructed but, apart from the plaques, has little else of interest. It can be viewed from the upstream side easily enough, and with a little scrambling over the rocks, on the other side also when the river is not in flood.

Pont Ponterwyd, 748809 (135)

The first major bridge over Afon Rheidol is at Ponterwyd, where the Llanidloes to Aberystwyth coach road passes over a lofty elegant bridge. It was bypassed in the early 1930s because the narrow roadway, of only eight feet (2.4m) at the crest of the arch, was insufficient for the traffic needs of the time. The span is seventeen yards (15.5m). The recent repointing, coupled with careful conservation work at a time when old

212

bridges were generally left to decay, means that the structure is well preserved for the future. Bollards placed at both ends confine its use to pedestrians only. There is doubt about its date of construction, but the mid to late-18th century is a good guess. There are more imposing single arch bridges in the old county, but this one is well worth a visit.

Pontnewydd ar Aeron, 507592 (146)

Pontnewydd *(Newbridge)* is by far the oldest bridge on Afon Aeron, but has been subjected to a great deal of patching and rebuilding on the downstream side. The arch rings on the upstream side are built of thin irregular stones and the original recess on this side is still retained, although it has been repaired with some new stonework in places. There is no recess on the other side, this having been removed when the bridge was widened to its present width of twelve feet (3.6m). There are two segmental arches, a hefty upstream cutwater, and small square flood openings in the approaches. The overall span in twenty-four yards (22m). The bridge is only a short distance from the A482, on the road to Cilcennin, and there is ample room to park at the southern end.

Pont Trefechan, Aberystwyth, 582814 (135)

The town of Aberystwyth was granted its charter in the middle of the 13th century, and it was of vital importance to have a permanent bridge over Afon Ystwyth. It is possible that even at this early stage in the towns development an attempt was made to build a stone crossing, but a combination of high tides and floodwater cause considerable havoc, and it was often necessary to erect temporary wooden piers in between a solid stone construction.

In 1540 one William John Voya left the sum of twenty shillings 'to the working of the bridge at Aberystwyth'. During the next three hundred years a number of bridges were built and replaced at regular intervals as parts collapsed during floods, or they fell into disrepair. Ogilby stated that the bridge at the end of the 17th century had eight arches, but in Rees' time it had nine. A drawing by Rowlandson in the mid 1790s shows a six arched stone bridge, but this was so badly damaged by 1798 as to require replacing, and a new wooden crossing was built by Lewis David for two hundred pounds.

Early in the 19th century this was replaced by a stone bridge of five arches, and there are several paintings of this structure to be seen at the Ceredigion Museum in the town. All the artists depict an imposing structure of four small arches and a large centre one. A wrought iron gas lamp was fixed on top of the centre arch, a feature retained by the designer of the present bridge, James Szhumper, who increased the number of arches to eight.

In 1885, a severe flood washed away the large centre arch and work began at once on the present crossing. The contractor, David Lloyd, was a local man, who obtained the stone from the newly opened quarries at Ystrad Meurig. Building work started from both ends, and in order to draw the attention of his foreman on the other side, a bell was rung. All work would cease and he was able to shout his orders across. The bell recently came to light, and has been presented to the museum.

The bridge takes its name from the suburb of Trefechan on the southern side. The three arches of equal size, superbly constructed in dressed stone, makes it well worth the effort to scramble to the foreshore on the downriver side to view it.

The iron gas lights are still in position, having been tastefully adapted for electricity without loosing any of their character. A plaque at the town end is difficult to read, but simply records the date of completion, 1888, and the builders name.

Pontarfynach, 743770 (135)

The original Welsh name was superseded during the Victorian era when the gorge became popular as a tourist attraction and the name The Devils Bridge, which had a suitably supernatural ring about it, was gradually adopted. The name arises from the many Welsh folk tales which involved the devil, and in this case he is reputed to have been involved in the construction of the lowest bridge.

Pontarfynach is one of the best known beauty spots in Wales, well served by roads and the Vale of Rheidol railway, and hundreds of visitors pay their fee to squeeze through the turnstiles to view this unique spectacle of three bridges, one above the other, every year.

The lowest of the three bridges, which is still a hundred feet above the foaming Afon Mynach, was probably built about a hundred years after Giraldus crossed over a rickety wooden structure in 1188. The builders were probably the monks of Strata Florida, who had lost one of their brethren whilst crossing the gorge.

The present lower arch is wider than the original; Wyndham in 1777 noted that it was 'scarcely twenty feet in span', and was 'a few years since in a very ruinous state'. The second bridge, with a span of twenty yards (18.3m), had been built over it in 1753. Jervoise is of the opinion that the masonry of the bottom bridge was widened on both sides during this construction, and that the present 'pointed arch was built inside the abutments of the second', in order to obtain sufficient strength and width for the second crossing.

During the first decade of the 19th century the Rev. T. Rees mentioned 'it is in contemplation to improve the upper (second) bridge by raising and widening it'. This improvement took place at the expense of Thomas Johnes of Hafod in 1814, and Hughes in his *'Beauties of Cambria'* (1823) stated that it had 'lately been improved, and the sides secured by cast iron railings'. These ornamental iron parapets have an inscription stamped into a rail:

Cast at Aberdare Iron Works 1814.

In 1867 an iron footbridge was constructed below the Jacob's ladder to replace an insecure wooden crossing, which enabled those who ventured down into the gorge to complete the circular trip up the other side in reasonable safety. A cast plaque has the inscription 'Aberystwyth Foundry 1867. Thos Stokes Engineer'. The distance from the top bridge to the river at this point is over five hundred feet (152m).

In 1901 Cardigan County Council set about constructing the present bridge. The designs submitted were considered by some Council members to be too formal, and a drawing instructor at Aberystwyth University was consulted to add what was termed as 'further embellishments'. These later proposed additions were not approved, and the bridge was built by the Morriston building firm of Rees and Kirby much along the lines of the original design.

About this time Cardigan County Council had started the practice of inserting plaques into all the newly built bridges, recording the date and the name of the County Surveyor. The plaque on the eastern parapet reads,

Erected by the Cardigan County Council 1901. R. Lloyd Surveyor.

A translation can be seen on a similar plaque on the western parapet.

Bearing in mind the large number of Victorian travellers and artists who visited the site, among them George Borrow, it is surprising to find that so few illustrations have survived. The one drawn by Gastineau is the best known, and has appeared in many books of the period.

Bridges of Ynys Môn (Anglesey)

Ynys Môn (The Isle of Anglesey) has a number of streams, but no significant rivers. Most of its bridges, apart from those crossing the Menai Straits, are small, insignificant, and fairly modern.

Pont Aberffraw, 355691 (114)
Jervoise considered this to be 'the most striking bridge' on the island, and it is certainly one of the oldest to survive without any alteration. It was built in 1731 and has one semicircular arch of eleven yards (10m) span and a roadway of ten feet (3m) width. It has long since been bypassed, and is now only used by visitors who wish to cross the shallow, but muddy, Afon Ffraw at this point.

Four Mile Bridge, 280784 (114)
This, the only other stone bridge of any historical importance, is so named because it is that distance from Caergybi (Holyhead). The present bridge is modern, but the structure in Pennant's time was named Rhyd-bont. This bridge was often in such a bad state of repair that it was only used as a last resort. Ogilby's direct route was across the sands, but he stressed that this was only available 'when the tide is out'.

The Quarter Sessions recorded the problems, and the cost of keeping the bridge repaired. In 1769 they ordered that 'Rhyd-bont Bridge be immediately put in sufficient repair', allowing seventeen pounds for this purpose the following year. More money was required in 1781, fifty pound being allocated early in the year, and a further eight pounds at the Michaelmas Sessions.

Pont y Borth *(The Menai Suspension Bridge)*

Pont Porthaethwy, or Pont y Borth as it is known locally, is probably the best known bridge in Wales. Seen from the Ynys Môn side, with the mountains of Eryri *(Snowdonia)* as a backdrop, it is a magnificent sight.

This masterpiece of bridge construction deserves a book in its own rights but space will only allow a few basic building facts and a brief look into the background of the venture.

There were plans to build a bridge across the Menai Straits long before Thomas Telford made the dream a reality in 1826, and this marvel of his engineering genius was not his first choice. The original plan was to build a single cast iron arch of five hundred feet, and one doubts if even his brilliance could have achieved such a construction. Even his second plan, a bridge of five arches with three of iron and two of stone, was very ambitious.

The contract took six years of constant work under the most appalling conditions, especially during the winter months. Even his workforce of weather hardened navvies, who received a constant supply of ale as part of their contract, had to have it topped up with spirits during severe working conditions. It was therefore not surprising that a number of accidents occurred.

The final approved plan was for a suspension bridge, a hundred feet (30.5m) above the high water mark, and with five hundred and seventy-nine feet (176m) between the towers. It was well beyond anything previously attempted, and there were many who doubted its feasibility. There were also the prophets of doom who predicted that it would collapse, if not under the first coach to cross, then certainly during the next gale.

The laying of the first stone on August 10th, 1819 was a low key affair as there was considerable local opposition to the project, notably among the ferrymen. There was compensation, Jane Williams being paid the handsome sum of twenty-six thousand, five hundred and fifty-five pounds when her ferry was made redundant.

There were no objections however from Viscount Bulkeley, whose quarries at Penmon supplied the stone at a rate of six pence a ton.

The island of Ynys-y-moch provided the base for one of the two hundred and fifty-three feet (46.6m) high towers, and a series of arches stretched to the shore, four on the Ynys Môn side and three on the other.

The masonry was completed by the autumn of 1824, when the critical task of hauling the sixteen giant chains to support the central span began. A large crowd had gathered, many expecting to witness a failure, but on

April 26th 1825 the first chain was raised successfully by a group of men operating a capstan. Telford watched from the Caernarfon side, and was so relieved that all had gone according to plan that he dropped to his knees in an act of thanksgiving, and was still in that position when a group of friends and well-wishers came to congratulate him.

It took ten weeks to hoist the remaining cables into position when a temporary planking was installed as a roadway.

This temporary pathway allowed the mailbags to be carried across before the bridge was properly completed. The festive activities that took place during the summer of 1825 made the actual opening in January 1826 something of an anticlimax.

The time of year was hardly suitable for public celebrations, and the authorities had waited so long for the crossing to be completed that they were not prepared to wait until morning before sending the first mail coach across. The London to Holyhead mail coach arrived in the early hours of the morning, and the driver battled his way across in the face of a rising westerly gale. The coach was crammed full of engineers and contractors who just wanted to be there for the privilege.

The Chester mail passed over the bridge at 3.00 a.m., but Telford was not present and missed the spectacle of seeing his bridge lit by oil lamps, giving it a somewhat eerie appearance. By morning the great man had made his appearance, arriving in a hired post chaise and welcomed by large numbers of sightseers. The bridge had cost one hundred and twenty-three thousand pounds to build, which was considered very good value at the time. Every user was charged a toll to cross. Even the main coaches, which were exempt elsewhere, had to pay half a crown one way. Private carriages paid two to three shillings, and foot passengers a penny. The rates were not cheap, but considerably lower than the ferry charges which just prior to the bridges completion was half a crown a wheel.

The bridge served as the vital link through to Holyhead and Ireland for over a century with only the need for regular maintenance. A gang of painters would take a year to apply three coats of paint to the top of the structure and the same time, suspended in cradles, to paint underneath.

Tolls continued to be charged to cross the bridge, and a tollhouse was built on the Ynys Môn side, occupied by a full time keeper who was assisted by temporary reliefs during the quiet periods of the night. They were in a position to wake the tollkeeper if anything out of the ordinary happened. He was not pleased when a circus crossed over in the middle of the night, and his relief woke him to ask the toll for an elephant!

There was a strict four and a quarter ton limit on all vehicles, which was quite enough for the early years of the 20th century. Buses were the only vehicles to exceed the limit, and it was decided that they could only carry a certain number of passengers. Tollkeepers were quite strict, some refusing to accept the drivers word on the number of passengers. They would board the bus and force the excess number to walk over, usually in pouring rain.

On the morning of January 10th, 1936 the readers of the *Western Mail* were greeted by the banner headline 'Menai Suspension Bridge Hangs By a Thread'. Something of an exaggeration perhaps, but a severe gale had blown the stop block which prevented the centre span from moving further than two feet out of its bed.

There was much local concern that the island would be isolated for some considerable time, and strong representation was made to the Government to undertake urgent repairs. Damage was not as great as first feared and traffic could still use the bridge while repairs were carried out. It was decided that all the chains should be replaced, but war intervened before the task of refitting could begin. It was decided to continue the work, but under great national secrecy, and an official photographer was employed to keep a detailed record of the work.

The reconstructed bridge was opened on January 1st 1941, having suffered very little traffic disruption. At the same time, tolls were abolished. The following inscription was chiselled into the tower:

Reconstructed 1938-40. Engineer Sir Alexander Gibb. Contractors Dorman Long and Co.

During the war, the gap under the bridge was used by a squadron of Lancaster bombers training for a low level flying mission. This was not as difficult a manoeuvre for experienced pilots as one would think. With a clearance of five hundred and sixty feet (171m) between the towers, and a hundred feet (30m) between the roadway and high water there was ample room for an aircraft like the Lancaster. The same could not be said for the Polish fighter pilot who flew his Spitfire under the metal opening section of Pont y Bermo!

Today over five million vehicles cross in a year, and Pont y Borth still remains one of the most popular attractions in Wales. The best viewing point is considered to be from the A4080, near Llanfairpwllgwyngyll. The point is marked on OS maps.

River Bridges of Gwynedd

It is quite impossible to record every bridge that has a rugged, ancient appearance in the old county of Caernarfon. The hard volcanic rock used to construct them is not subjected to the same degree of weathering as the shale and limestones used in other parts of Wales, and in most cases they are undatable. With such a wide range of stone available, and a pronounced lack of timber in the hilly areas, one would expect to find stone built bridges much in evidence from times when the lowlands were still using timber.

But the bridges of this part of Snowdonia, strong and sturdy though they might be, lack the character and individuality of those seen elsewhere in Wales. I have been unable to discover any with recesses or circular flood openings, and the construction techniques seem to be common to most of them. Jervoise found little to interest him, and devoted only six pages of his book to all of Ynys Môn and Caernarfonshire. A few bridges bear inscriptions, but one would have expected many more in an area so well known for its slate cutting skills.

A few bridges date from the latter part of the 18th century, but the majority are of mid to late 19th century construction.

The Bridges of Northern Gwynedd

Conwy Suspension Bridge

This is a spectacular crossing of the Conwy Estuary on the Chester to Holyhead road, but however graceful this bridge may have been, it was not without its critics, and has always been upstaged by the Menai crossing.

The Conwy estuary was the second most difficult natural obstacle Telford had to overcome as he pushed through the mountains of north Wales without exceeding a gradient of 1 in 22. A ferry had carried the coaches over Afon Conwy since the Irish Ferries were routed through Holyhead, and there was an inevitable loss of life during storms. The worst loss occurred on Christmas Day 1806 when the ferry, commanded by an inexperienced ferryman, was caught in a squall. Of the thirteen crew and passengers, only two survived.

It became obvious that a bridge was long overdue, but matters dragged on for more than a decade after the disaster before finances, and the expertise of a man of Telford's calibre, made the project a reality. The crossing could have been made further upstream, but it was necessary to pass through the town of Conwy, at which point the estuary was wide and solid foundations difficult to find.

Telford's plan was a five hundred and fifty yard (503m) causeway, and bridge towers built on a smally rocky island called 'yr Ynys' in front of the castle. There were a number of objections to the plan; the long causeway would be a hazard to navigation and the bridge itself would affect ship building on the Conwy, although it turned out that they had little effect on either. Turner had recently painted the castle from across the estuary, and a number of lesser known artists had found the view much to their liking. They objected strongly to a bridge ruining the view, and it was to compensate for this loss that the two towers of solid masonry were built so as to conform with the castle. The bridge was started in 1822, with the same contractors as were building the Menai bridge. The overall span between the towers was three hundred and twenty-seven feet (100m), and it was necessary to blast a way through the rock to gain access to the town.

The bridge was opened in 1826 and served as the only road crossing until it was replaced in 1959. Its close proximity to the castle marred its appearance, and it cannot be regarded as an elegant suspension bridge.

It is now in the care of the National Trust, one of very few bridges in that category. You will have to pay for the honour of walking over it, but at least it receives the care it deserves.

Pont y Cim, 443523 (115)

Pont y Cim over Afon Llyfni is the only bridge marked as an antiquity on the O.S. maps. It is reputed to have been built as early as 1612, but there is considerable doubt about this date, and somewhere towards the end of the 17th century would be much more realistic. There is hardly anything recorded about its early history because neither Llwyd nor Pennant mentioned it, and Jervoise passed with only a brief reference to its size.

He did however include a photograph which shows a single segmental arch, and mentions the unusually low parapets. It is nine feet (2.7m) wide and has a span of twenty-one feet (6.4m).

Since his time some repairs have been necessary which has resulted in one end of the arch being squared off, giving the bridge an unfortunate, lop-sided appearance.

Pont Llyfni, 435526 (115)

A mile downstream from Pont-y-Cim the A499 crosses this newer bridge that bears the date 1777. It has three segmental arches and is sixteen feet (5.9m) wide and twenty-eight yards (25.6m) in length.

Pont Dolbenmaen, 507430 (115)

This bridge is now bypassed, but it remains in good condition. Its massive single arch and long abutments were built of glacial boulders. It is an imposing structure, but contrary to its appearance, it is no earlier than the late-18th century.

Bont Newydd, 663720 (115)

This bridge, near Abergwyngregin, is also marked on the O.S. maps as an antiquity, although it is not earlier than the mid-18th century. It has a single segmental arch with a span of fifteen yards (13.7m) and a width of thirteen feet (3.9m).

Pont-y-tŵr, 627660 (115)

A bridge was mentioned by Pennant, but it is very doubtful whether it was the present structure, which has been widened from an original eleven feet (3.3m) to nearer nineteen feet (5.8m). It has three segmental arches, and is one of several similar bridges around Bethesda. Pont Penybenglog has the remains of an earlier arch underneath, but neither are of great age. Halfway Bridge (607690) further down Afon Ogwen is now a modern crossing, but this is the only bridge of which I am aware to carry such a name.

A short distance upstream a fine single arch bridge leads to the Penrhyn Quarries. This was built of slate slabs by the local quarrymen.

Pont Beblig, 492621 (115)
An insignificant bridge typical of the many built during the mid-19th century. This one differs only in that it carries a plaque stating that it was built in 1844 and that the architect was John Lloyd and the contractor Lewis Williams.

Bont Newydd, 484599 (115)
Here is another bridge with that familiar name, but in this case a village developed around it that took the name Y Bontnewydd. Leyland, Ogilby and Pennant mentioned crossings that were here prior to the present bridge, that was built in 1840. It was built by the same contractor as Pont Beblig, and has a single arch of twenty-six feet (7.9m).

Pont Llanystumdwy
This massive bridge of three segmental arches was considered by Jervoise to be the most 'interesting bridge in Caernarfonshire'. The original width was only about nine feet (2.7m), but widening on the downstream side has increased this to twelve feet (3.6m). The date of the earlier section of the bridge is uncertain. The massive cutwaters on the upstream side are worth nothing. These have now been ruined by additional building to support a new pedestrian roadway. When viewed from downstream, the bridge is still an imposing structure of considerable character.

Bont Fechan,
Situated on Afon Dwyfach, south-west of Llanystumdwy, it now has a roadway of thirteen feet (3.9m), having been widened from the original eight feet (2.4m). The four segmental arches span twenty-eight yards (25.6m).

Afon Conwy and its Tributaries

Afon Conwy, with its tributaries Afon Machno, Afon Lledr and Afon Llugwy, is crossed by as wide an array of bridges as you will find anywhere in North Wales. They range from the unique lintel types over Afon Lledr, the so called 'Roman' packhorse bridge over Afon Machno, to Telford's bridge at Conwy. The famous cast iron Waterloo Bridge, and the ninety foot span arch at Rhydlanfair, which is the longest in North Wales, are among those 'listed', and although most of the railway crossings are modern, Pont Gethin is a superb example of a Victorian stone viaduct.

Pontargonwy, 778337 (124)
This, the first of the eighteen bridges that span Afon Conwy, is just below the source high up on Y Migneint and has been rebuilt and possibly widened during the last century, but still retains its three square lintel arches. Jervoise ignored it, but it is of an unusual type to be found spanning a river on a main road.

Pont-rhyd-y-saint, 844489 (116)
This bridge was named by Llwyd as 'Pont Ysypthi', and carried the old road over Afon Conwy at Ysbyty Ifan. Jervoise considered it 'attractive', and suggested it was built early in the 18th century. Local tradition claims that its construction took place after a woman was drowned while crossing the ford. The original bridge had two arches about twenty-three yards long (21m) and nine feet (2.7m) wide, but it has been recently rebuilt and widened recently and is no longer of any interest.

Pontrhydydyfrgi, 847514 (116)
Also known as Pont-pant-glas and Pontlima, it was built in 1788 and consists of a high wide arch over the river, and a much smaller arch alongside, in what is really the abutment. A little upstream is a small bridge that crosses into the Foelas estate, which was at one time used by the locals. The owner of Foelas at the time objected to this intrusion on his ·privacy, and financed the building of Pontrhydydyfrgi. Although it still only carries a side road it has recently been repointed and strengthened.

Pont Padog, the next crossing downstream was built early in the 19th century as part of Telford's A5 construction. It has a single arch of just under fifty feet (15.2m), and has also been repaired recently.

Pont Rhydlanfair, 829524 (116)

The old road from Ysbyty Ifan to Llanrwst crossed Afon Conwy at this point. The present bridge dates from 1780 and was built by Robert Griffiths, a local builder, after two other attempts had failed. It has a span of around ninety feet (27.5m), making it the longest in North Wales, and a width of fifteen feet (4.6m).

Fenton, in 1810, recorded it as 'a new bridge of one very lofty arch and of a wide span over the Conwy'. It is now listed, and has like many other bridges in the area been extensively repaired recently.

The large wooden former on which the arch was built was assembled in Chester, and carried in sections to the site by a haulier named Thomas Edwards, better known as Twm o'r Nant.

It appears that the two failures were the result of natural disasters rather than avoidable building mistakes. In the first instance, flood water resulted in debris building up around the wooden former, causing it to collapse. The second mishap was also a result of collapsed woodwork, this one occurring as the arch was nearing completion. The third attempt proved successful, the bridge being completed in 1787. As at Pontypridd it was a case of third time lucky. Twm o'r Nant was subsequently recruited to carry the former to where part of it was used to build Pont yr Alltgoch.

John Thomas wrote a famous englyn to Pont Rhydlanfair:

Llun enfys hysbys yw hi – llun camog
Llun cwman y milgi;
Llun 'C' uwch cerwyn freci,
Llun cwr lloer yn llyncu'r lli.

Pont Newydd, Pentrefoelas, 863513 (116)

Two bridges some fifty yards apart share this common name. They cross Afon Merddwr, and are described by Jervoise as 'a lofty arch of a ten foot span, and a much flatter arch'.

Pont-Llan, Penmachno, 791505 (115)

This bridge, considered by Jervoise to be of a rather unusual design, has three elliptical arches, a span of sixty yards (55m) and a width of fifteen feet (4.6m). A plaque on the parapet states that it was the work of 'I. Hughes and Harry Parry of Caernarfon 1785'.

Two miles downstream there is a modern bridge called Pont y Pandy (807528) but alongside are the remains of a packhorse bridge known locally as a Roman Bridge. It is eight feet (2.4m) wide and only the arch ring remains. It is definitely not of Roman origin.

Pont-sarn-ddu, 711516 (115)

This bridge is often called a Roman bridge after the nearby railway station which is marked on the maps as 'Pont Rhufeinig'. It is of course not Roman, but has been built along the lines of a clapper bridge, which Jervoise found to be a 'particularly interesting structure'. This type of construction is unique to Dyffryn Lledr, although some are quite modern.

The illustration shown in Jervoise's book shows rough stone piers supporting stone slabs, but these have since been replaced by concrete strips. The upstream piers are of a solid construction and Jervoise was correct in assuming that they had been rebuilt, but those on the downstream side are disintegrating and covered in vegetation.

It is doubtful if there ever was a parapet of any significance, but if there was it has long been replaced by a chain link fence which is now badly rusted. In all there are eight piers supporting the six openings, and a further four in the approaches serving as flood openings. Jervoise records a width of ten feet (3m), but it is now only about eight feet (2.4m). The surface has been tarmaced, making the crossing suitable for farm vehicles.

A battered notice on a gate alongside the bridge appears to have been there at least as long as the wire parapet. It states that the land around is private, which makes viewing from the downstream side, at least, impossible. A public footpath branches off a short distance away on the upstream side. Although wandering from it is against the Country Code, some bridge enthusiasts may feel inclined to take the risk, and walk the few yards to the bank to see this quite remarkable structure.

Pont-y-pant, 756539 (115)

Jervoise considered this to be the oldest of the clapper or lintel type bridges in the valley, and his illustration would confirm this. It has since been completely rebuilt and the stone piers now carry steel girders and concrete posts.

A far better example can be seen in the footbridge that crosses Afon Lledr a little higher upstream (at 746527). It is most unusual that Jervoise did not mention this crossing for he could hardly have missed seeing it, and although the wooden section over the river is recent, the long abutments with their square flood opening on both sides are at least a hundred years old and probably much more.

The remains of another lintel bridge, which consisted of fairly large stone piers supporting a wooden roadway, can be seen a little way above Pont-ar-ledr (797542).

Pontyrafanc, 798546 (115)

The bridge has been incorrectly translated to Beaver Bridge. Although the Welsh word for a beaver is in fact 'afanc', the bridge was named because of its close proximity to Llyn yr Afanc. According to a folk legend this pool was once the haunt of a water monster of the Loch Ness variety, and this is also known in Welsh as 'afanc'. The bridge was built in 1805 and prior to that, the road followed the western bank. It is a massive stone structure that is typical of others than span Afon Conwy, with an arch of sixty-eight feet (20.7m) span. It was completely repointed in 1978.

Pontgyfyng, 735572 (115)

Pontgyfyng, the narrow or restricted bridge, is still only twelve feet (3.6m) wide. It was built in 1800 when a new road was being forced through the mountains to Bangor. Its single span is thirty-four feet (10.4m), and the view of the rapids from it is quite spectacular after heavy rain.

Miners Bridge (Pontymwynwyr), 780569 (115)

This bridge is a reconstruction of an earlier crude method of crossing the river by miners, to reach their workings on the far side. It is little more than a wooden bridge that has been laid at a sharp angle like a ladder across the river. It is included only because of its popularity as a tourist attraction.

Waterloo Bridge, (Y Bont Haearn), 799557 (115)

This well known cast iron bridge was designed by Telford to carry his A5 road over Afon Conwy at Betws-y-coed. It was completed in 1815 and carries a cast iron inscription in the same manner as Brynderwen Bridge, these being the only iron bridges in Wales to use this attractive method of recording the date of construction as part of the design. They read:

This arch was constructed in the same year the battle of Waterloo was fought.

Another interesting feature are the iron national emblems of the four home countries.

The iron was cast at Plaskynaston Foundry. The span is one hundred and eight feet (33m), and its the seventh largest cast iron bridge in Britain. It was inevitable that extra strengthening was required to cope with modern traffic demands, and it is surprising that it was not bypassed. The Welsh Office planners decided to construct a concrete roadway above it, which is not only distracting but also hides some of the ironwork.

The original structure has suffered many accidents, one in particular in 1952 when an US army tanker crashed through the railings and ended up in the river.

The bridge is a listed monument, and will no doubt receive the protection it deserves.

Y Bont Fawr, Llanrwst, 799615 (115)

The bridge, now marked as an antiquity on the O.S. maps, was probably built around 1636. There was an earlier wooden crossing which was declared unsafe in 1627.

Sir Richard Wynn of nearby Castell Gwydir became responsible for the building of the first stone bridge, and there is a strong tradition that it was designed by Inigo Jones. There is a distinct lack of documentary evidence to this claim, but it is possible that he did at least have some involvement in its construction. Inigo Jones, born Ynyr Jones, changed his name when he moved to London. He was a friend of the Wynns, and it is quite conceivable that he supplied the original plans. There is considerable doubt however over whether he supervised any of the construction.

It was ten years before the original stone bridge was completed, the cost being met equally by the people of Caernarfonshire and Denbighshire, Afon Conwy being the boundary between the two counties.

It has been suggested that the centre arch collapsed on the opening day because the locking key stone had been inserted upside down. This mishap was blamed on the large quantities of mead drunk by the workmen (which was in fact part of their building contract). Rebuilding started at once, but this time the workforce were instructed to drink nothing stronger than buttermilk, and for some years later it was known as the 'Buttermilk Bridge'.

Pennant in his *Journeys to Snowdonia* in 1781 stated that the third arch had been rebuilt in 1703 by a 'very inferior genius'. There are suggestions that the centre arch was also rebuilt at around that time.

There are three arches covering a total span of about sixty yards (55m) and it is only thirteen feet (4m) wide. The centre arch is sixty feet

(18.2m) wide by twenty-four feet (7.3m) high, the side arches are forty-five feet (13.7m) wide by fifteen feet (4.6m) high. With such a difference in dimensions the roadway has to run up a steep camber, resulting in traffic chaos when motorists are unable to see advancing vehicles until they meet in the middle. This has resulted in the bridge being referred to as 'Pont y Rhegi', *(The Swearing Bridge)*, a name that reflects the moods of some motorists as they struggle to cross during the busy summer months.

Because two vehicles cannot pass each other, a local inhabitant could sometimes be seen sitting on the parapet directing the traffic, which either improved or aggravated the situation depending on his skill, and the co-operation of those he was attempting to usher over the bridge.

Most of the time, motorists manage to free themselves with only the inevitable mutterings and curses, but one particular jam led to an incident that resulted in the media becoming involved in the traffic problems of this sleepy North Wales town.

A van driven by a local man, came over the brow of the bridge to be confronted by a car driven by a visitor from the other side of the English border. Assuming that he had the right of way, and backed by the fact that his van was the largest of the two vehicles, he carried on only to find that the other driver had no intention of reversing.

The two vehicles screeched to a halt, inches apart; driving seats were quickly vacated, and a heated argument took place. Eventually the law appeared in the form of the local constable who, having told the participants off in a manner only a village bobby knew how, proceeded to book them both for obstruction.

When the case came before the magistrates, both drivers put forward a spirited defence. The van driver claimed that he had the right of way, being over halfway across, but the car driver was adamant that he was only obeying the Highway Code, which advises motorists not to reverse into a main road. He claimed that traffic from the town end had priority.

With feelings running high and the locals already taking sides in the argument, the magistrates stepped in and brought the proceedings to a close by finding both defendants guilty, and fining them five pounds each. The matter did not end there because an appeal was considered, and it became obvious that the long term solution to the problem would have to be temporary traffic lights.

The old house on the western side is Tu Hwnt i'r Bont, and is in the care of the National Trust. The constant flow of people from it adds to the traffic problem.

There are two inscriptions on the bridge, one bearing the arms of the

Prince of Wales, the other the date of the original construction in 1636.

The recesses above the cutwaters were installed to serve a less traffic congested era, but still prove to be of much benefit to pedestrians today.

Pont-y-pair, 793567 (115)

This much sketched, painted and photographed bridge structure is one of the best known stone bridges in North Wales. The English translation of 'pair' is cauldron, and anyone looking over its massive parapets into the waters below will easily imagine a steaming cauldron.

The builder of the original downstream side was Hywel Saer-maen *(Hywel The Mason)* around 1500, but Pennant states that he died before completing the task. The bridge was widened by about nine feet (2.7m) around 1800 and Fenton, who crossed in 1810, states that the widened part could be clearly seen in the middle arches.

There are five arches in all, each of a different span as the foundations were built onto convenient rocky areas in the river bed. A number of prints and paintings of the bridge are available, as well as a wide range of postcards, most depicting it covered in ivy. In recent years it has undergone something of a facelift and is now a listed structure.

Pont ar Ledr, 797542 (115)

The original bridge was built by Hywel Saer-maen before he attempted Pont-y-pair, but the present bridge dates from around 1700. Jervoise remarks that it resembles Pont-Llan Penmachno, and that the middle pier is 'unusually narrow'. It was also noted by Pennant and Fenton. There are two arches, again of different spans, for no other reason than the location of suitable rocks to serve as foundations. The bridge has now been widened and the eleven foot (3.3m) roadway is suitable for the minor road it now carries. It also has a flood arch and cutwater, and an overall 'rustic' appearance. The view of the rushing Afon Lledr from it, particularly in autumn when the leaves are changing colour, are breathtaking, and a number of coloured Edwardian postcards can still be found.

The Bridges of Meirionnydd

The Bridges of Afon Dysynni and its Tributaries

Afon Dysynni is one of those rivers that breaks all the rules. It emerges from Tal y Llyn lake, which is fed by the many small streams and rivulets that flow down from the slopes of Cadair Idris and other surrounding mountains, but instead of making straight down the valley for the sea, it turns sharply right through a geological fault at Abergynolwyn into Cwm Llanfihangel-y-Pennant before eventually reaching its destination via the Broad Water mud flats at Tonfannau.

The valley itself is beautiful, surrounded by steep hills and rocky crags, particularly Craig y Deryn, but it is not a big or impressive river. During its short journey it is crossed by a number of stone bridges. Some like Pont-y-cwrt at Abergynolwyn and Pont Iago over a tributary on the B4405 are modern and hardly worth a second glance. Others like Pont Ystumanner, although fairly new, are at least worth closer inspection, if only to be included as foreground in what has become a favourite snapshot scene. Of the remainder, there are four that are worth the effort to get out of the car and take a closer look.

Pont Llaeron, 701049 (135)

Pont Llaeron is one of less than half a dozen original pack horse bridges. It can only be seen by those who are prepared to don climbing boots and face a hard uphill climb. Set in the hills above Abergynolwyn, it was once on the track between the Dysynni and Dyfi valleys. Although marked on the 1:50,000 maps, it is not easy to find on the ground, due largely to the high degree of afforestation in the area that has all but obliterated the original track.

A metalled road, not really suitable for cars, leads from Abergynolwyn to the site of the old Bryneglwys quarries, or you can follow the path alongside the river. Where these two meet, you will have to follow the public footpath signs up a boggy and not too obvious track which, with a little bit of luck, will bring you to the bridge.

During the early years of this century a walk to Pont Llaeron was a popular excursion and it featured prominently in postcards of the area. It was in good condition, and was still virtually intact when I first saw it in the 1960s. Since then, those who gain pleasure from defacing and damaging structures of historical value have succeeded in removing all the parapet stones, which has increased its width from the original six feet (1.8m) to nearly eight feet (2.4m). The length still remains ten yards (3m).

Even after the damage it has suffered, it is still well worth the effort to see it. No one has made much of an attempt to date it, but speculative guesses put it at around the mid to late-18th century. Machynlleth Quarter Sessions recorded Pont Llaeron was out of repair in 1756, which confirms it is of much earlier origin than the suggestions that it was built in the mid 1800s by Edward Pughe, to carry slates to Pennal.

The river forms a cateract just below the bridge, and a little further on the remains of sluice can be seen, where the water was diverted into a reservoir which supplied the quarry workings. It was still marked as a lake on the first O.S. Landranger Series Maps, although it had been breached years earlier. The earthworks still remain, giving some indication of the amount of water required to power all the machinery.

Those who are prepared to make the journey after a period of hard frost will not only find the boggy ground much harder, but will see the ravine below the bridge transformed into an enchanting ice grotto.

Pont Cedris, 693082 (124)

The first bridge of any interest on Afon Dysynni itself is Pont Cedris, and it has several features worth noting. It is surprising to find two arches of such different lengths, probably because it was the only place the builder could find suitable foundations in the valley soil. The arches are very low, the smallest being almost horizontal, and it has been necessary to support part of it with timber struts. There are also square flood openings which are now almost silted up. Built of outcrop slate slabs, much the same as Pontarddyfi, it also has a string course, and a masons mark which Jervoise interpreted as a trowel and hammer. He also stated that the date 1865 was to be seen, but it is no longer there. The bridge is probably a little older, dating from around the early-19th century. The roadway was thirteen feet (4m) wide but widening took place on the downstream side during the winter of 1998/99.

Until fairly recently a rickety but attractive wooden bridge served Cedris Farm, a little downstream, but progress has demanded its replacement by a sturdier but ugly metal and timber crossing.

Pont y Garth, 635071 (124)

At this point Afon Dysynni has increased enough in width to require two arches to cross it and this bridge, which is built of rough stone slabs, has a particularly rustic appearance. Had it not been for the lavish use of cement to reinforce the centre cutwater, it would be an attractive sight. The stone slabs set into the parapet to assist access to the river bank are an interesting feature, and there is a pleasant walk upstream. It was built in 1797 at a cost of one hundred and three pounds.

Pont Dysynni, 599048 (135)

The river has by now widened enough, especially with a high tide, to require four arches. This bridge, now bypassed, is another rugged stone built structure of late eighteenth or early nineteenth century design, and is thirteen feet (4m) wide. It has no special features, but the view from downstream with the backdrop of mountains is a fine one.

The Bridges of Afon Dwyryd

Afon Teigl and Afon Cynfal join Afon Dwyryd in the neighbourhood of Ffestiniog, and Jervoise mentions Pont Teiliau Isaf and Pont Tal-y-bont. Both have now been extensively rebuilt, and are now too modern to be of interest.

Pont Dôl-y-moch, 685415 (124)
This is without doubt the most important bridge in the area, and is marked on the Pathfinder Series Maps as an antiquity. It was built about 1790, but has the appearance of being much older. Of its four segmental arches, two have been recently repaired on one side with the usual distracting result, but this was necessary to preserve the structure.

There are recesses, two of which have badly worn stone seats, and the parapet is exceptionally low at under two feet (60cm) in height. The width is just eight feet (2.4m), although the road signs state it is less, no doubt a precautionary measure. It still carries a secondary road and is quite serviceable. It must rank among the best preserved and most interesting of the ancient bridges of North Wales.

A little downstream from the bridge, Afon Dwyryd receives Afon Cynfal which is spanned a short distance upstream by a bridge named by Jervoise as Pont Dolrhiwfelen. This is possibly the name of the farm it served. It has been out of use for some considerable time and the track is well grassed over. A look underneath will reveal two arches of some seven feet (2.1m) span, and it is difficult to determine which is the oldest. The hard volcanic rock of the area makes many of the buildings that have no dates or documentary evidence attached to them virtually undatable. Apart from recording that it was fifteen feet (4.6m) wide Jervoise did not offer any other comments, which is surprising as it is an important bridge that carried the track from Gellilydan to the mansion at Dol-y-moch. The earliest part probably dates from about the same time as Pont Dol-y-moch. Llwyd recorded a bridge called 'Pont y velin Rhud' in this area, and it is possible that this is the same one.

Pont Maentwrog, 666407 (124)
Pont Maentwrog is now bypassed and will hopefully survive. It has three elliptical arches of triple keystones, which makes it similar in shape to Pont-Llan, Penmachno, which was built in 1785, and it is probable that Pont Maentwrog was erected at about the same time.

Pont Briwet, 619383 (124)

This wooden trestle railway crossing over the Dwyryd estuary was the Cinderella of the Cambrian Coast Railway, having been completely upstaged by the spectacular Pont y Bermo and to some extent by the lesser crossing over Afon Dyfi. Of the many publications relating to the history of the Cambrian Railway, no reference of importance is made to this bridge which must have been erected without any of the problems of needing an opening section, as was necessary for the other two.

The name is a mystery.

The road toll-bridge that runs alongside was added at a later date, and whether this was erected during repairs or replacement of the piers is not known.

The Bridges of Afon Mawddach
and its Tributaries

Penmaenpool Toll Bridge *(Tollbont Penmaenpŵl)*, 696185 (124)

The bridge was built by the Penmaenpool Bridge Co. Ltd who came to an agreement with the Barmouth Harbour Trust early in 1879, and work was completed by the following year.

The Harbour Board objected to the original plans, which only allowed an opening of twenty feet (6.1m) between the timber piles. Their concern was that the abandoned shipbuilding yard at Maesygarnedd, upstream of the proposed site, would reserve its shipbuilding activities. The owners of the shipyard assured the inquiry that they had no intention of building any more ships at the yard, but provisions were still made to allow for the passage of boats if it ever became necessary. Permission for the construction of the bridge was given on the condition that the centre opening was increased to thirty feet (9.1m), and that provisions were made to convert it into a drawbridge.

Shipbuilding on the upper reaches of Afon Mawddach was never revived and the conversion never took place. The building of the bridge put the ferry out of business, but pleasure craft continued to cruise to and from Y Bermo. One of these vessels was involved in a tragic accident in 1956 when it was caught on an ebb tide and collided with the bridge, resulting in several lives being lost.

The railway station has now been converted into part of the nearby hotel and the signal box serves as an observation platform for the bird sanctuary. The bridge is still an useful short cut for motorists, although it is no longer necessary to go all the way through the town of Dolgellau to reach the other side, which is something of an advantage for those who feel strongly about having to pay a toll.

Bont Newydd, 772202 (124)

It may come as something of a surprise to find a bridge named Bont Newydd *(New bridge)* listed as an antiquity, but this is the case of this huge single arch structure that carries the B4416 over Afon Wnion. The original was of great age, but it has been much repaired and widened on the upstream side to give a roadway of sixteen feet (4.9m). The arch has been cemented underneath, which is frustrating for historians as it makes it impossible to locate the original stonework. There are, however, enough of the original sections left to make it worthy of inspection. This is more than can be said for Pont Llanrhaeadr, the next one upstream, which has been completely rebuilt in recent years.

Pont Helygog, 792196 and Pont Rhyd-y-gwair, 795205 between Pont Llanrhaeadr and Brithdir are interesting small single arch bridges built of boulders, and are of undetermined age. Moss covered and rustic in appearance, they are seldom visited, and are ignored in favour of those on the more popular 'tourist' routes.

Pont Fadog, 607226 (124)
This is a fine two arched bridge that once carried the coaching route from Bont-ddu to Harlech through the lonely Bwlch y Rhiwgyr. An inscription carries the date, 1762, and the word Saer.

The track that now leads to the bridge is unsuitable for cars, but it is only a short walk from the Cors y Gedol Burial Chamber.

Pont Sgethin, 633235 (124)
This bridge is marked on the O.S. Maps, and a quick glance will show that it is in one of the wildest and remotest parts of North Wales, some two and a half miles upstream from Pont Fadog. Those who struggle up the rough, and often wet, track to reach it will find a small arch built of rough stone, some eight feet (2.4m) wide over a shallow river, and will wonder why it was built at all. It has all the appearances of a pack horse bridge and no doubt it served as such, but it was also on an earlier coaching route, although it is hard to believe that wheeled vehicles did use it.

Pont Figra, 668192 (124)
The bridge is best described as a massive stone embankment across the gorge of Afon Cwmllechen above Bont-ddu. The river flows through a small lintel type opening at the bottom, and although insufficient at times of flood, the structure is still intact.

It was built to carry a tramway about 1860, when the Figra and Clogau gold mines starting producing in earnest, and it is eight feet (2.4m) wide and thirty-three feet (9.4m) long. The tramway is now a pleasant public footpath but it is difficult, and in fact dangerous, to attempt to descend into the gorge to view it properly.

Pont ar Eden, 727248 (124)
There was a stone bridge here, according to Llwyd, early in the 18th century but the present structure is probably from a century later. It has a fine single stone arch which on a still morning is mirrored in the pool

below. The wheeled traffic that most use it now are Forestry Commission Lorries and, in recent years, prospectors for gold at the Gwynfynydd mine, all of whom find its twelve foot (3.6m) roadway a tight squeeze.

Pont Dolgefeiliau, 722269 (124)
This is another fine old bridge over Afon Eden, which carried the A470 at right angles over it, causing many problems for drivers of long vehicles until it was recently bypassed. It has now been bollarded and will hopefully be left to age in peace.

Pont Abergeirw, 768291 (124)
This is a single arch stone bridge of undetermined age over Afon Mawddach, in a remote area. It has long abutments with square flood openings on the southern side, and the parapets have been replaced by iron railings. Much of the construction is of dry stone, giving it a very rustic appearance. A small bridge nearby, with a modern roadway that leads to a chapel, is also of interest and is of a fair old age.

Pont Pen-stryd, 732305 (124)
This narrow single arch bridge built of river boulders has a particularly antiquated appearance. It has recently been repaired and repointed, probably due to the increased mining activity at the Gwynfynydd mine, which it connects with the one time hamlet and chapel of Pen-stryd. It is a very attractive bridge with a hump back and square flood openings. There is no through road although turning is not a problem.

Pontargain, 752328 (124)
This single arch bridge is tucked into the hillside that carries the mountain road from Trawsfynydd to Llanuwchllyn. The width is just sufficient for cars, but the hairpin bend requires care. During the war the area was used as an artillery range and subjected to much destruction, and it was some years before the road was re-opened due to the dangers of unexploded ammunition. The bridge survived intact and the downstream river bank, which is the best viewpoint, is also a popular picnic spot.

Pont Gwanas, 768167 (124)
The Old Pont Gwanas was bypassed in 1930. Although not named by Ogilby, it was marked on his route, and the original structure probably dates from that time. It is now double its original width, having been

rebuilt on the downstream side, and extended to fifteen feet in width. The upstream side has cutwaters and two segmented arches with single arch rings. The downstream side has only a pilaster and double arch rings. The construction is of undressed boulders, and both earlier and later work has now blended to form an attractive bridge. It was inspected by Jervoise, who recorded that it 'has fortunately been saved'. It has recently been repointed and the grassed roadway can be approached from the lay-by alongside.

The new bridge is a little upstream, and was probably the last traditional stone bridge to be built. It has two segmental arches, and recesses above the cutwaters. A slate plaque on the downstream parapet has the following inscription:

Merionethshire County Council, Gwanas Bridge, opened by the Right Honourable Herbert Morrison Esq. M.P. Minister of Transport 26 June 1930.

Both bridges span Afon Clywedog, and recent flood prevention work has resulted in the cutting back of the trees on the banks, which now allows the old bridge to be viewed from the trunk road.

Pontarddibyn, 761179 (124)

This bridge, a mile and a half downstream from Pont Gwanas, has a single pointed arch with double arch rings and a ten foot (3m) wide roadway. The parapets are high, and have a decorative square pillar built on top. The driveway to Plas Caerynwch, situated a little upstream, starts at the bridge, and there are two reasons why it is possible that the current bridge was built at the same time as the hall. The bridge is much later than the others on Afon Clywedog, and has been very well built of dressed stone, which makes it possible that Caerynwch and the bridge share the same builders. The bridge is on a sharp bend on the B4416, and is the starting point for the Torrent Walk which is a delightful stroll alongside the river as it thunders down a deep ravine.

The last bridge on the river, before it joins Afon Wnion, also dates from around the same period and also has a single arch, but no special features. Those doing the round trip of the Torrent Walk will pass over it.

Pont Cefn-coch, 765175 (124)

Situated between Pontarddibyn and the old Pont Gwanas, this small rugged stone bridge was probably built at around the same time as the latter was widened. The rough track leading to it is not a public right of way, and it must be stressed that it is on private land and cannot be visited. However it has no special features and is no different from the many other stone bridges that span the streams of upland Meirionnydd. It does not justify causing annoyance to the landowner by sneaking through the attractive wooden gate alongside the A487, just past Cross Foxes, to see it. It is, incidentally, quite probable that this gate was the one used by the Mawddwy Turnpike Trust, which had a tollgate nearby.

Bont Fawr Dolgellau, 729180 (124)

This is considered to be one of the oldest bridges in the district, but it has been rebuilt and repaired so often that all that can be seen of the original construction is the downstream portion of the three middle arches. This part was built early in the 17th century when there were ten arches, but these were reduced to seven when the railway was built halfway through the last century. Some rebuilding of the other arches also took place at this time. The two arches at the southern end show no signs of widening, having arches of the same type on both sides, suggesting that they were completely rebuilt to match the others.

According to Jervoise, the date A.D. 1638 was still legible on one of the southern arches when he inspected the bridge in 1931. He goes on to record that the original width was only eleven feet (3.3m), but it has been increased during rebuilding to fifteen feet (4.6m), and the length of the seven arches is seventy yards (64m). The railway section of the bridge was replaced with a concrete crossing during the building of a bypass that runs along the old rail track. Two of the arches are almost silted up, but the bridge is unique in that it is built on a sharp slope to compensate for the difference between the heights of the banks of Afon Wnion.

The upstream side has been completely overshadowed by an iron footbridge, and the only suitable viewing point is from a recreational area known as the Marian, downstream.

Pont Llanelltud, 718194 (124)

The bridge at Llanelltud is the only one of note over Afon Ganllwyd, having five, three centered arches spanning a distance of seventy-six yards (70m) and a roadway, that does not appear to have been widened, of fourteen feet (4.3m). Edward Llwyd noted Pont Lhan Elhtyd, and Ogilby's route from Welshpool to Caernarfon crossed here, but he does not refer to a bridge. Earlier crossings took place further east at Llanfachreth.

The date of construction is uncertain, and it could well have been rebuilt over a period of many years like Bont-fawr, Dolgellau. Jervoise has little to offer on its building either. It has not carried traffic for many years, first being bypassed by a temporary girder bridge with lights, and in recent years by a massive concrete construction a little downstream. It is possible to drive up to the bridge by taking the road to Cymer Abbey from the A494, but bollards prevent wheeled vehicles from crossing. The view from downstream with the backdrop of trees and mountains is a fine one, particularly in the late evening when the light is low.

During one of my recent visits it was gratifying to see that the local authorities were sufficiently concerned about its upkeep to send two of their employees, armed with waders and ladders, to scrape the vegetation from its crumbling stonework.

The Bridges of Dyffryn Dyfi

Afon Dyfi is only some thirty miles long, and yet passes through scenery so spectacular and varied that it is considered by many to be among the most beautiful rivers in Wales. From its source in Creiglyn Dyfi, under the crags of Aran Fawddwy, it passes through the wild and rugged mountains of Mawddwy, meanders its way past the fertile plains of Mathafarn, before joining the sea through its beautiful estuary at Aberdyfi. Those who prefer to see it from the comfort of a car can travel along the A489 and A470, which run down the southern side and are still known locally as Y Tyrpeg; or the more adventurous can risk their shiny vehicles along the narrow leafy lanes of the old coaching road on the northern side. The view from either side of the valley is pleasant, especially in the early morning or late evening when the sun is low.

For those who prefer to see its beauty the hard way, the one hundred and eight mile long Dyfi Valley Way, provides a bird's eye view from the hills above.

Those that come to look at bridges may at first glance feel disappointed, the stone bridge at Machynlleth being the only one of interest between Mallwyd and the sea, a distance of over twenty miles. However, at the top of the valley the two parishes of Mallwyd and Llanymawddwy more than make up for the shortages lower down. In this comparatively small area can be found five bridges of great age and historical significance. All are bypassed, difficult to find, and in some cases even more difficult to approach, but all are well worth the effort.

Pont Nant-yr-ehedydd, 904124 (125)

The bridge can be seen on the O.S. map as two thin lines below the sharp hairpin bend, a couple of miles east of Mallwyd on the A458. Ogilby named it as Nantaradith Bridge which, considering some attempts, was a good effort on his part. He also mentioned was a Nantedegodl Bridge a little further east, which was actually Pont Nantdugoed, but this was rebuilt in 1923 and is of little further interest.

Jervoise in 1931 records that Pont Nant-yr-ehedydd is now disused and lies at the bottom of a deep ravine. It is also known locally as Pont Penelin y Diafol, *(Devil's Elbow Bridge)* and was, by all accounts, the cause of many accidents for horse drawn vehicles due to its lack of parapets, steep hill and the sharp bends on the approaches. The road now takes a much higher route, having cut into the side of the hill probably during the Turnpike Trust improvements in the 1840s. The new bridge was also rebuilt in the 1920s, and is a high, single arch construction but with no other interesting features.

The old bridge is a superb example of dry stone bridge building techniques, its single arch having held together for at least three hundred years, and may even be the original mentioned by Ogilby. It has no parapets, is a little over eight feet (2.4m) wide, and is about twelve yards (11m) long.

The ravine is thickly wooded and even with the main road only a short distance away, it is a forbidding place. One can imagine what it was like on a cold October evening in 1555 when Lewis Owen, the High Sheriff of Merioneth, was ambushed and killed by the notorious Gwylliaid Cochion Mawddwy *(Red Bandits of Mawddwy)*. Legend tells us the ambush took place at a spot named 'Llidiart y Barwn' *(Barons Gate)* further along the road, but there are those who still believe that it was here at this dark and dismal spot that he met his death.

The area is still much the same. Several trees of varying size struggle to find root upon the bridge, and during my visit a large ash had finally given up the struggle and collapsed across the approaches, thankfully without causing any apparent damage to the masonry.

The bridge actually crosses Afon Clywedog, much to the confusion of anyone trying to find it without local directions, but it is named after a nearby farmhouse, which in turn was named after a small stream that flows into the river higher upstream. A large stone building that was once a woollen mill now serves as a barn, and stands alongside.

Two large stone blocks have been built across the western approach which, according to a member of the Home Guard during the war, were intended as tank traps in the event of an invasion!

The bridge deserves to be restored and, with some effort and the co-operation from the landowner, this can be carried out with only a little difficulty as the stone work is in remarkably good condition. Parking in the area is a problem, the only safe spot being a small layby for one car opposite the much needed 'Reduce Speed Now' sign on the eastern side. The bridge can be reached by following the old road down into the ravine.

Pontywrisgen, 820131 (125)

The bridge is a little to the east of Mallwyd on the Welshpool road and, like the others on this stretch, was rebuilt as part of a major road building contract in the early 1930s. It carries the road over Afon Cleifion on a high and attractive stone arch, but has no other feature of special interest.

The present bridge has retained the name, which has been marked on all O.S. maps up to the present 1:5000.

In 1806 the Welshpool to Aberystwyth coach 'hit a bridge at Mallwyd', causing injury to the outside passenger as 'they were thrown to the rocks below'. Although the exact place was not named, it is reasonable to assume that the accident took place here, and not as has been suggested at Pont Mallwyd, where anyone 'thrown onto the rocks' would hardly have survived.

Pont-y-Pennant, 905202 (125)

There are three stone bridges between Dinas Mawddwy and the steep mountain pass of Bwlch y Groes, none of which are of any great age or particular interest. Pont y Pennant is the first over the infant Afon Dyfi, a small single arch of dressed stone, probably built at the beginning of the last century when, according to Colt Hoare, the road over to Bala was being built.

Pont Melin Cerist, 847156 (125)

The old road from Dinas Mawddwy to Dolgellau used this bridge before a new stretch, which avoided the twists and turns, was built in the 1930s. Recently this has been further bypassed by the new A470, and the bridge is now tucked away out of sight, well away from the main road.

It is very similar in construction to Pont Nantyrehedydd and probably dates from the same period, but it is in much worse condition. Part of the upstream arch has collapsed and been replaced by a concrete girder. What remains of the single arch is built of rough undressed stone, and the original small parapets have been covered over with many years of road surfacing materials. At present, all that stands between the user and the river is a stretch of rusting wire.

The bridge crosses a small tributary of Afon Cerist. Alongside can be seen the remains of the mill that gave the bridge its name, which was destroyed during the first lot of road improvements. The twentieth century has arrived in the form of an unsightly caravan park close by, and the old bridge can only be seen from the river side, causing much scrambling and slithering accompanied by scratched hands and torn clothing. The bridge can be driven over by turning to the right from the A470, just after Dinas Mawddwy while travelling in the direction of Dolgellau.

Pont Mallwyd, 857122 (125)

The present bridge spans Afon Dyfi in a single arch at one of its narrowest and most picturesque points, the gorge below Mallwyd. Its age has been the subject of much discussion locally, but it is now generally accepted that it is not one of the three bridges built by Dr John Davies, the Rector of Mallwyd, in the mid 1630s, but almost certainly the next one to be built at the site.

The only written evidence to the building of earlier crossings is that found on the back of the title page of the 1568-1702 church register, which appears to date from the first half of the 17th century. It does not mention the involvement of Dr Davies, but it does mention the building of three bridges, two over Afon Dyfi and one over Afon Cleifion, between 1633 and 1637.

The inscription, written in Welsh, refers to the construction of a bridge of timber on five stone pillars at Mallwyd in 1633. It also refers to an earlier bridge, called 'Ryfyngan', built in the same place and swept away in 1574. The bridge that replaced it suffered the same fate in 1614. A new position was chosen for the next bridge, which consisted of two stone piers, but it lasted less than a year. A position further down the gorge was selected for the next attempt, but this was washed away in 1632.

It is evident that there have been crossings at this point since medieval times. Mallwyd was an important staging post on the road from Welshpool to Machynlleth, which until the early years of the 19th century ran down the western side of the valley.

There is no reason to suppose that the bridge of timber on five stone pillars built in 1633 lasted any longer than its predecessors, and the present single arch between two rocky outcrops was probably finished and in use by the turn of the 18th century at the latest. There is, however, no record of its construction, and the earliest reference to its existence is that by Richard Colt Hoare who in 1808 states in his diaries that he:

> crossed the Dovey near Mallwyd over a picturesque bridge, and the only one in a long distance between this place and Machynlleth.

The Cambrian Travellers Guide of 1813 describes it as 'a lofty mountain bridge of a single arch, grey with lichens. One side ornamented with ivy'. The only early illustration of which I am aware in that by J.G. Wood in his *Principal Rivers of Wales* (1813).

Sometime during the latter part of the last century the parapets were either replaced or repaired, and iron railings placed on top. By the time I was familiar with the bridge, a favourite place for the school ramble in the mid 1940s, they had broken off, and it was a long way down to the river.

When the two bridges further downstream were destroyed by the floods of 1964, it became the only means of access to the west side of the river for a distance of some twelve miles. During the next year or so, until a new bridge was built, a stream of light vehicles inched their way cautiously down the narrow road and across it, without doing too much damage to its structure or their paintwork. Farm tractors and stock lorries found it heavy going, but it was an useful short cut and they continued to use it after the new bridge was completed at Aberangell.

In an attempt to reduce this flow of heavy traffic the Highway Authorities rebuilt the parapets, bringing the width in between them back to the original eight feet (2.4m) or so. This move would have been welcomed if the building had been carried out in river boulders to match the original structure, but to carry out the work in sawn pieces of quarry waste when there was so much suitable material available from collapsed buildings locally, was little short of sacrilege. The public outcry had hardly died down when the growth of ivy was removed and further beauty treatment added in the form of a hideous cement wash.

The bridge is not listed, which is understandable as there are many similar structures to be found throughout Wales, but it is sad that one of the main features of what is still a popular beauty spot has been ruined.

Pont y Cleifion, 862127 (125)

The bridge spans Afon Cleifion, which is the name given to the lower stretches of Afon Dugoed. There is no doubt that this is one of the original stone bridges built by Dr John Davies. The inscription in the church register states that 'Pont y Cleifion was built of a stone arch in 1637'. It spans a rocky chasm and remained in use until a new road bridge was built in 1845. This has since been replaced by a massive concrete crossing, and thankfully the old stone arch below was saved, although no restoration work has been carried out to date. It is covered in ivy and thick layers of earth which should be removed, if only to prove if the initials J.D. are, as claimed, set into the roadway in white stones. If a parapet did exist, it has long since been removed, and both ends have been fenced off as some form of safety gesture.

A stile leads down to the river bank, which is the best viewing point, but care is required, especially in wet weather. The single arch is more pointed than semicircular, and its width is about eight feet (2.4m). The overall length works out at around twenty feet (6.1m), but until this important bridge is cleared of its tangled growth, and properly restored, its true dimensions are pure speculation.

Pont Minllyn, 060138 (125)

The A470 improvements have resulted in a concrete crossing over Afon Dyfi at Minllyn, just south of Dinas Mawddwy, bypassing the stone bridge of 1846. The original name was Pont Ffinant, and the O.S. Map of 1880 quotes both names.

There was a crossing here that was marked on Saxtons map of 1678, and Ogilby called it Pontrusk having mistaken it for Pontywrisgen, on his route from Welshpool to Caernarfon. There were probably other crossings here before Dr John Davies came along with the money to build what is described in the church records as Pont y Ffynant. This was built of timber on three stone pillars in 1635. It is often believed that Dr Davies, a benevolent man, built these bridges for the sole benefit of his parishioners. There is another tradition that he undertook the work after he and his servant had been thrown from their horses after they had lost their footing while crossing the river.

Once again we are faced with a dispute over the age of this bridge. The records state that the one built in 1635 had a timber roadway. There are thoughts, but no evidence, that the arches were added shortly afterwards.

J.G. Wood described it as 'An ivy clad bridge of two arches' in 1813, but Richard Fenton chose to ignore it, as did Colt Hoare and the others who must have passed over it. Jervoise describes it as having two segmental arches, a span of twenty yards (18.3m) and a width of eight feet (2.4m). He also states that it:

> 'has no parapets, and little now remains expect the arch rings, but it is an interesting relic of the past and should be preserved at all costs. It is certainly in decay.

It remained in decay for over fifty years defying the ravages of floods and the probing onslaughts of the roots of a tree that had sprouted from the centre pier. It was only after local pressure was brought to bear that some preliminary repair work was carried out. The bridge is now in the care of Cadw, the Welsh Ancient Monuments Department, and at the time of writing it is being restored to its early 20th century condition. Jervoise would have been pleased with the result.

773099 (124)

This is an interesting tramway bridge that once served the Aberllefenni Slate Quarry, and is still in use as a road bridge. Built of sawn slate waste in the 'clapper' style, it consists of six square openings and is now much weathered, having possibly been built as early as the 1860s. It is thirty yards (27.4m) long and nine feet (2.7m) wide. Bridges of this type were common throughout the North Wales Slate Quarries, often consisting only of piers of waste slate, with the rails slung across the top. Very few have survived to become road bridges.

Pont Llwyn-gwern, 754045 (135)

This is an elegant bridge of dressed stone, with touches of classical design in the form of arch and urn forms that are set into the abutments. Two large circular columns at one end suggest that it was built by the Llwyngwern estate and quarry to connect with the Corris railway on the western side of Afon Dulais. The railway was completed by the early 1860s which dates the bridge at this, or a slightly later, date.

The name, Llwyngwern, beautifully carved on a slate plaque, has been set into the downstream parapet, but years of tar and chippings have begun to encroach on the bottom of the slab. When viewed from the river bank, the single arch is impressive.

There are no other bridges of interest above this point. Evans Bridge the next one up is quite modern, and Pont Abercorris is a small stone arch of no significance, although Llwyd mentions a bridge here which was probably a wooden structure.

Pont Glan Gwynedd, 753024 (135)

This bridge, over Afon Dulais, does not have an original name and also appears as Pont Melin-y-ffordd on the O.S. leisure maps. The crossing was marked on Ogilby route up the western side of Afon Dyfi, but at that time it was either a ford or a wooden bridge. The present stone bridge was probably built early in the 19th century, possibly at the same time as the nearby Pontarddyfi.

The bridge has been built of local outcrop slate, or the poor quality Red Vein from the nearby quarries, and is showing signs of deterioration. It is held together by massive iron bolts, passing straight through the structure. Only one cutwater remains, the others having been crudely patched with concrete.

It is now fifteen feet (4.6m) wide, which suggests that it has been widened, although there is no obvious indication of this. The three segmental arches of different sizes span a thirty yard (27.4m) width of river.

Pontarddyfi, 745019 (135)

Afon Dyfi is the natural boundary between Gwynedd and Powys, and there was a crossing at this point in the middle ages. In 1533 a London

248

merchant named Geoffrey Hughes left six pounds thirteen and fourpence in his will 'towardes the making of a bridge at the town of Mathanleth'. Either the sum was insufficient to construct a solid bridge, or floods took their toll, for in 1681 it was reported to the Sessions that 'Dyfi bridge in the Hundred of Mochunlleth was insufficient'.

The Ogilby route crossed here, but he gives no details of a wooden bridge. For most of its length between Mallwyd and the tidal estuary, a mile below Machynlleth the river has low banks and is easily fordable, with over a dozen marked on the earlier six inch maps for this stretch. It has even been suggested that the Romans crossed here, but in all probability it was downstream opposite their fort at Pennal.

The present stone bridge was built in 1804, from much the same material as that over Afon Dulais, but Pontarddyfi appears to have fared a little better. Richard Fenton described it as 'a noble building with five large arches'. The bridge remains much the same today as when it was built, having escaped flood damage due to the surrounding low lying area, which allows the river to overflow its banks before it reaches dangerous heights on the bridge.

Fenton's description of the number of arches is correct, although the word large is exaggeration. The piers are narrow with a pilaster over each of the small cutwaters, and a string course at road level.

The fine salmon pool below the bridge has been much abused by poachers, who have attempted to remove its occupants by all the illegal means, ranging from spearing to dynamiting. In 1925 a confrontation took place with the river bailifs, that resulted in cracked skulls and broken limbs. It is still a popular spot with fisherman, although the number of fish in the pool have decreased considerably in recent years. The bridge is best viewed from downstream on the Machynlleth side, and the small hamlet of Pen-y-bont, with the thickly wooden slopes above it, makes a pleasant setting particularly in spring and autumn.

Pont Gelli-goch, 733992 (135)

Several rivers flow into Afon Dyfi to the south of Machynlleth, and although there are many stone bridges in the area all are fairly recent with one exception. Pont Gelli-goch, named after the nearby house, can be seen from the Aberystwyth road some two miles from Machynlleth alongside the side road to Glaspwll. It is without doubt the oldest bridge in the lower stretches of the valley. It spans a small stream in a single arch of only about four feet (1.2m) in height, but it is difficult to determine if the channel, at some time in the past, was a little deeper. The overall width is sixteen feet (4.9m), with a widening of four feet (1.2m) on the downstream side. The length is twenty feet (6.1m), and there are no parapets.

A gateway at one end would suggest that the grassed track, now barely visible, is still used by farm vehicles, but it was on an earlier road from Machynlleth to Derwen-las. It was probably bypassed as early as the 1840s, and sections of the road are now difficult to find.

The bridge has been built of outcrop slate, and the older upstream side has partly collapsed and is well weathered. The arch rings on the addition are of neatly dressed slate and in reasonable condition, and unless the stream is high it is well worth venturing underneath.

Attempts at dating are, as is often the case in this type of bridge, purely speculative with late-18th century being the most likely. It should be noted that it is on private farmland.

The Bridges of Afon Twymyn

Afon Twymyn rises in the wild moorlands of Pumlumon, flows through the remains of the lead mining village of Dylife, throws itself over one hundred foot (30m) high crags into Cwm Pennant, before meeting Afon Dyfi at Glantwymyn, which was horribly Anglicised to Cemaes Road with the coming of the railway.

Pont Crugnant, 887958 (136)
The road that leads from Llanbrynmair up the Pennant valley and over to Llanidloes, past the Clywedog dam, is not a popular holiday route. Many of the bridges have been either widened or bypassed, and some have been rebuilt but are still worthy of viewing. Crugnant flows down to join Afon Twymyn along a deep ravine over which this bridges carried a road that until a few years ago was only suitable for farm vehicles. It has since been widened and pinned in the same manner as Pont Glan Gwynedd, but still retains much of its original character. The only safe point from which to view is the upstream side, and its huge elliptical arch and sweeping parapets are worth noting.

Pont Pennant, 880977 (136)
This bridge is well maintained, and has a projecting keystone, a large string course and an attractive single arch.

Pont Dolgadfan, 886012 (136)
Situated in the village of the same name this is an interesting single arch bridge. It has been widened on the upstream side and, for those who take the trouble to look underneath, the difference between the old and new sides are very apparent. It has the weathered look of a bridge that has stood on a drovers route for about two hundred years.

Pont Cringoed, 887013 (136)
This bridge is now bypassed and is covered in vegetation. Its single arch appears to be still in reasonable condition, but it is unlikely to remain in that way for long.

Pont Glyn-yr-hwrdd, 913018 (136)
This is a single arch bridge of uncertain date over Afon Iaen at Dolfach, east of Llanbrynmair. It is built of rough stone, and before the new road down the Talerddig gorge in the 1820s, it was the link between the village and the drovers route at Bontdolgadfan.

251

The bridge is eight feet (2.4m) wide and is probably the original stone crossing, although I was unable to reach the river to view it from below because the fast flowing river speeds down a steep and narrow gorge. The attractive house nearby used to be a fulling mill.

Pont-y-comins, 845030 (136)

The sharp hairpin bend and bridge at Comins Coch have avoided improvement probably because they are not on the recognised north south route. It is similar in construction to Pontarddyfi, but has only one arch, and was possibly built at the same time perhaps by the same builder.

The original road bridge was a wooden construction known as Pont Goch Walcog, and was forever in a poor state of repair. In September 1653 the Montgomeryshire Grand Sessions heard 'that the bridge over the river Twymyn within, and at the conjunction of the parishes of Darowen and Kemes called Pont Goch Walkog, leading from the parish of Llanbrynmair to Machynlleth is altogether ruinated and ought to be repaired and made up by the inhabitants of the aforesaid Parishes of Darowen and Kemes.

If the repairs were ever carried out they must have been very shoddy, and they were ordered to be repeated regularly during the years that followed.

The present bridge was built by the Turnpike Trust early in the 19th century. A large arch built on a sharp hairpin bend, it has somehow escaped serious damage to its parapets from heavy lorries, and is long overdue for replacement. There is nothing significant about this bridge, but a good viewing point is through the arch of the massive railway bridge a little downstream, which was built from stone extracted from the cutting at Talerddig, and is also worthy of interest.

Sources

R. Christiensen, *Forgotten Railways of North Wales* (1983).

James Page, *Forgotten Railways of South Wales* (1979).

Hugh McKnight, *Shell Book of Inland Waterways,* (1975).

E. Jervoise, *The Ancient Bridges of England and Wales* (1936 & 1976).

H.P. Richards, *William Edwards, Architect, Builder, Minister* (1983).

K. Mortimer Hart, *The Conwy Valley and the Lands of History* (1987).

William Coxe, *Historical Tour of Monmouthshire* (1801).

J.G. Wood, *Principal Rivers of Wales* (1813).

T. Rees, *Topographical and Historical Description of South Wales* (1819).

Thomas Pennant, *Tours of Wales/Journey to Snowdonia* (1778 & 1781).

Henri Gastineau, *Wales Illustrated* (1831).

Daniel Defoe, *Tour Through the Whole of Britain* (1724-26).

B.H. Malkin, *The Scenery, Antiquities, and Biography of South Wales* (1803).

Theophilus Jones, *History of Brecknock* (1809).

S.C. & A.M. Hall, *The Book of South Wales* (1859).

Historic Taff Valleys, Merthyr Historical & Naturalists Soc. Vol. 2 & 3 (1982 & 86).

Edward Llwyd, *Parochialia* (1708).

History of Carmarthen, Vol. 2 (1939).

Chris Barber, *Exploring Gwent* (1984).

Welsh Tourist Board, *A Glimpse of the Past.*

C. Green, *Cambrian Railway Album* (1977).

S. Hughes, *The Archaeology of the Montgomery* (1981).

Edward Pugh, *Cambria Depicta* (1816).

G.J. Williams, *Hanes Plwyf Ffestiniog* (1830).

R. Haslam, *The Buildings of Wales* (Clwyd 1979) (Gwynedd 1983).

The Journals of Richard Colt Hoare, 1793-1801.

P. Baughan, *The Chester and Holyhead Railway,* Vol 1 & 2 (1972).

Herbert Williams, *Railways in Wales* (1981).

R.A. Stevens, *The Brecknock, Abergavenny and Monmouthshire Canals* (1974).

Edward Wilson, *The Ellesmere and Llangollen Canal* (1975).

S. Hughes, P. Reynolds, *Industrial Archaeology of the Swansea Region* (1988).

P. Hockey, *Caerleon, Past and Present.*

Montgomeryshire Bridges Vol. 15 & 16, Montgomeryshire Collections.

Counties Quarter Session Records.

The Montgomeryshire Grand Sessions, 1650-60. Compiled and published by the National Library of Wales, 1996.

Dewi Davies, *Bridges of Breckonshire*, Cambrian Printers (Aberystwyth) 1992.

Brecon Museum Archives.

Glossary of Bridge Terms

Abutment: Position where the arch meets its solid lateral support.

Accommodation Bridge: Bridge over a canal to allow movement of livestock.

Arches: Part of the bridge that support the roadway.

Arch Rings: A single or double course of stones that forms an arch.

Aqueduct: Artificial water channel on an elevated structure of masonry. In bridge terms it usually refers to a series of arches carrying a canal over a river or a valley.

Bascule: Hinged lifting bridge, usually found on a canal.

Bowed bridge: Lattice girder bridge with top raised in a curve.

Brick Lined: A line of bricks under a masonry arch.

Buttress: Vertical members projecting from a wall to stabilize it, and to resist lateral thrust.

Cast Iron: Hard and brittle iron, cast in a mould to the required shape.

Clapper Bridge: Bridge made of large slabs of stone resting on rough piers.

Chamfered Arch: Where the face of the arch projects beyond the rings; often used as a decorative feature.

Cutwater: The pointed or rounded form of a bridge pier, usually found on the upstream side.

Engineers Bricks: Dense bricks of uniform size with high crushing strength and low porosity, usually dark purple in colour, and used for railway viaducts and bridges.

Flood Apertures: Openings, usually circular, in the abutments of a river bridge to relieve flood pressure. Flat openings can also be found in approach walls. Not to be confused with openings in haunched constructions, which are used to ease upward pressure on the keystone.

Girder: A large iron beam. A box girder is a hollow box section. A lattice girder is a braced iron framework structure.

Haunches: Also known as spandrels. Roughly triangular spaces between an   and its containing rectangles, or between adjacent arches.

Projecting Keystone: Where the keystone projects through the arch rings and or stands proud of the arch face.

Keystone: Centre stone in an arch, tapered in shape, and which locks the arch in position when pressure is applied from above.

Pier: A large masonry or brick support for an arch.

Recess: Built over a cutwater at road level to enable pedestrians from being struck by wheeled vehicles on narrow bridges. (Also known as 'stepasides' and alcoves.)

Semicircular: Half a circle.

Segmented: Part of any plane not passing through the centre of a circle.

Splayed Parapet: Protection wall on a bridge built leaning slightly outwards to add width to the roadway.

String Course: Fragmented stone course projecting from the face of bridge.

Skew Bridge: Bridge set at an angle to road, river or canal.

Underbridge: Where track runs under the bridge, Overbridge is the opposite.

Viaduct: Long bridge structure, often in a series of arches or piers.

Voussoir: Stones that make up an arch ring.

Pilaster: Rectangular column, often seen as a feature on the outside of a parapet.

Statistics

Longest Single Span Stone Bridge.
The longest in south Wales is Pont Llandeilo, at around one hundred and forty-five feet (44.2m) span. It is about five feet (1.5m) longer than the famous structure at Pontypridd. Pont Rhydlanfair at ninety feet (27.5m) is the longest in north Wales.

Longest Stone Bridge
Crickhowel bridge, with its thirteen arches, spans one hundred and forty yards (128m).

Longest Single Span Iron Bridge
Bigsweir bridge on the Wye, with a span of one hundred and sixty feet (48.8m), is the longest; followed by Brynderwen bridge at Abermule at one hundred and nine feet (33.2m), a foot (30cm) longer than the famous Waterloo bridge in Betws-y-coed.

Oldest Iron Bridge
Pontycafnau at Merthyr, built in 1793, is considered to be the oldest, but there are others built near that date.

Oldest tramway bridge
Pont Pwll-y-Llygod over Afon Gwendraeth Fawr was built around 1770, and is probably the oldest surviving.

Railway Viaducts

Cefn Mawr Viaduct is the longest with nineteen arches covering one thousand five hundred and eight feet (460m). It is also the highest at one hundred and forty-seven, and also the oldest, built in 1848.

The longest wooden trestle estuary crossing is Pont y Bermo with its one hundred and thirteen sets of piers and metal swing section, which covers eight hundred yards (731.5m).

The longest metal railway bridge is Hawarden Bridge at around four hundred and thirty feet (131m).

Aqueducts

The longest and highest is Pontcysylltau, at one hundred and twenty-seven feet (38.7m) high and one thousand and seven feet (307m) in length. The oldest is Pont-fawr, Pont-rhyd-y-fen, built to carry water to an iron works in 1823, although it now carries a road.

Highest Stone Bridge

Excluding railway viaducts, bridges over gorges are the most likely to qualify. It is said that the river bed is five hundred feet (152.4m) below the top bridge of Pontarfynach. No information is available, and short of dropping a plumb line over the parapets it is difficult to come up with a reliable answer.

Least Used Bridge

This was probably a railway viaduct at Rhydfelen in Glamorgan. This lattice girder bridge appears to have been used only once, to carry a ceremonial train in May 1909, and was never used afterwards until its removal in the late 1930s.

Commonest River Name

There are eleven rivers named Dulais on the Landranger maps, and six named Clywedog.